Non-verbal Reas

Eleven Plus
Secondary School Selection

Non-verbal Reasoning
8 Practice Papers

Standard and Multiple-choice Format

E

This book belongs to

Guidance notes for parents

These practice papers can be completed as standard or multiple-choice tests.

Multiple-choice Tests

Answers are entered onto the answer sheets at the back of the book. The actual test would be marked by a computer but, for the purposes of these practice tests, you will need to mark it yourself. It is important for your child to treat it like the real thing and record an answer in the appropriate box by drawing a clear line through their chosen box with a pencil. Mistakes should be carefully rubbed out and not crossed out since in the actual test this would not be correctly recorded by the computer.

Standard Tests

Ask your child to circle the answers as instructed in each section. Mistakes should be crossed through with a single line and the correct answer written clearly.

Marking and Feedback

The answers are provided at the back of this book. Only these answers are allowed. One mark should be given for each correct answer. Do not deduct marks for wrong answers. Do not allow half marks or 'the benefit of the doubt', as this might mask a child's need for extra help in the topic and does not replicate the real exam conditions. Always try to be positive and encouraging. Talk through any mistakes with your child and work out together how to arrive at the right answer.

Timing

This testbook contains 8 practice papers. Each paper should take about 30 minutes, however it is more important that a child completes the paper accurately and does not rush their answers. Children will speed up naturally with practice.

Practice Paper 1.

There are 35 questions in four sections on this paper. You have 30 minutes to complete this test.

Circle your answers carefully on the answer sheet or place a mark in the multiple choice answer box on the separate sheet.

Section A

On the left of the page is a sequence of figures in five boxes. One of the boxes is empty. This box can be filled by only one of the figures in the five boxes on the right.

Choose the figure that you think will best complete the sequence and circle the letter on the answer sheet, or mark the appropriate box on the multiple choice answer sheet.

Example:

A B C D E

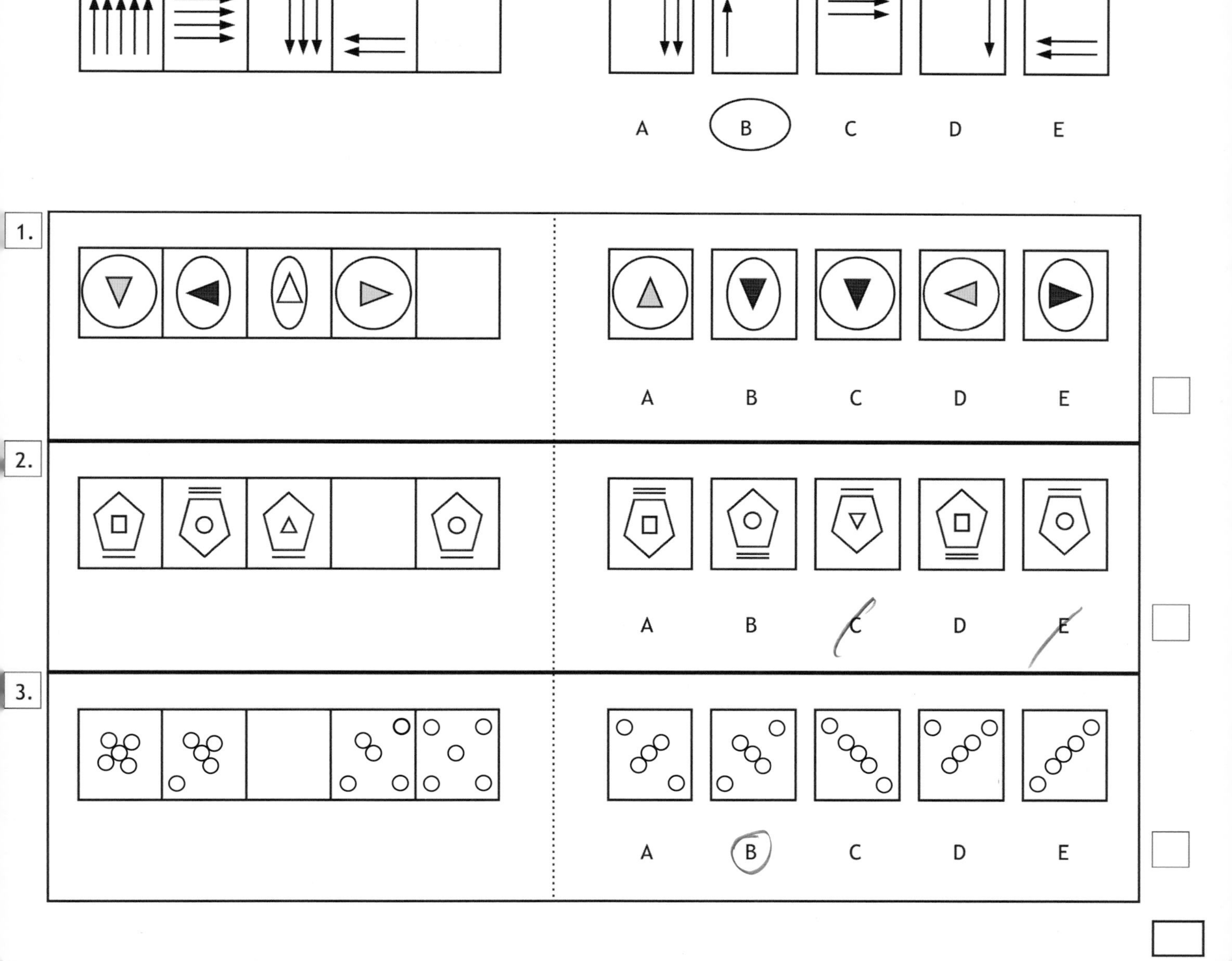

Page 1.2

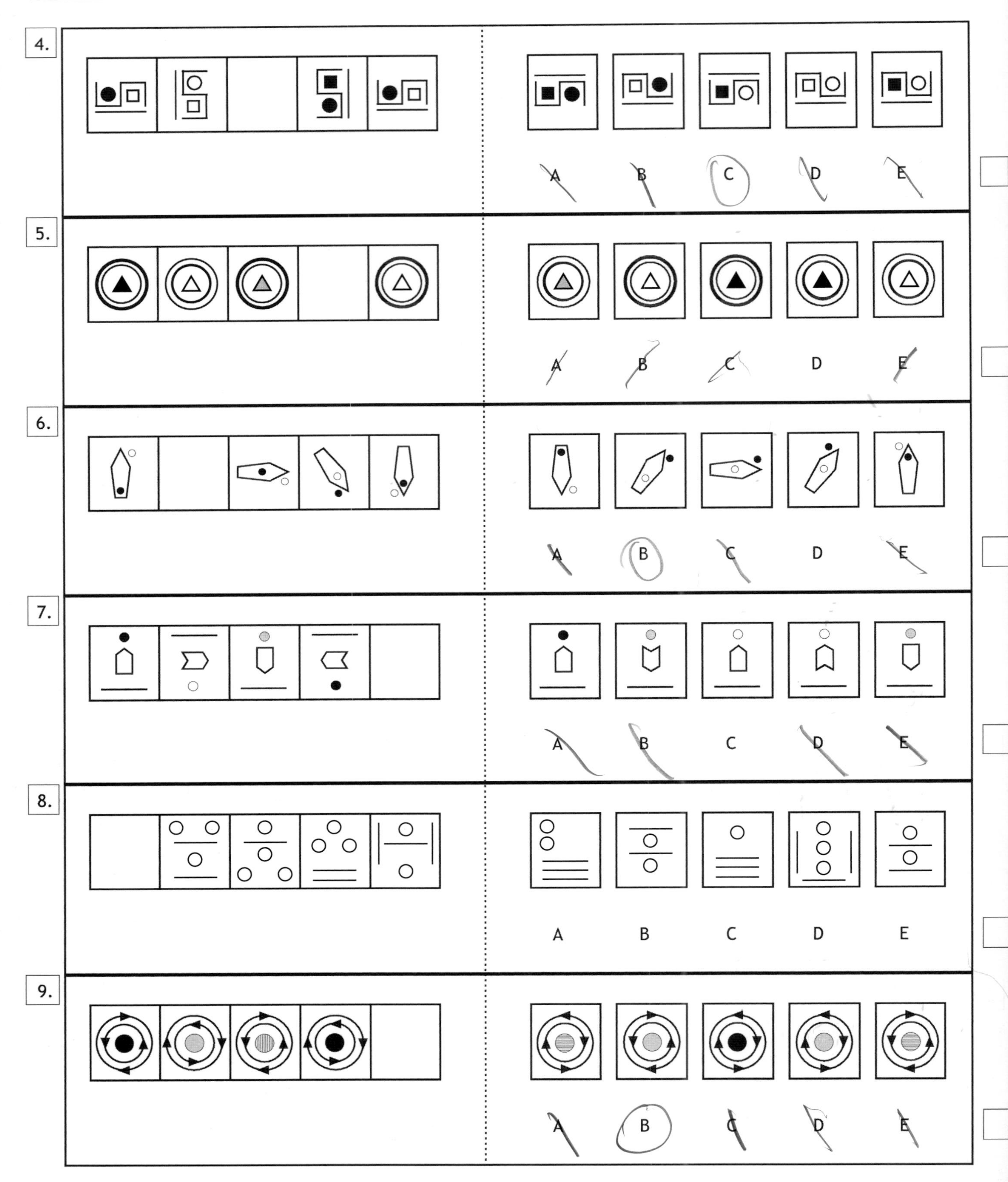

Section B

There are figures drawn in three sections of the large square on the left hand side of the page. One of the small squares is empty. This square can be filled by only one of the five boxes on the right.

Choose the box that you think will best complete the large square and circle the letter on the answer sheet, or mark the appropriate box on the multiple choice answer sheet.

Example:

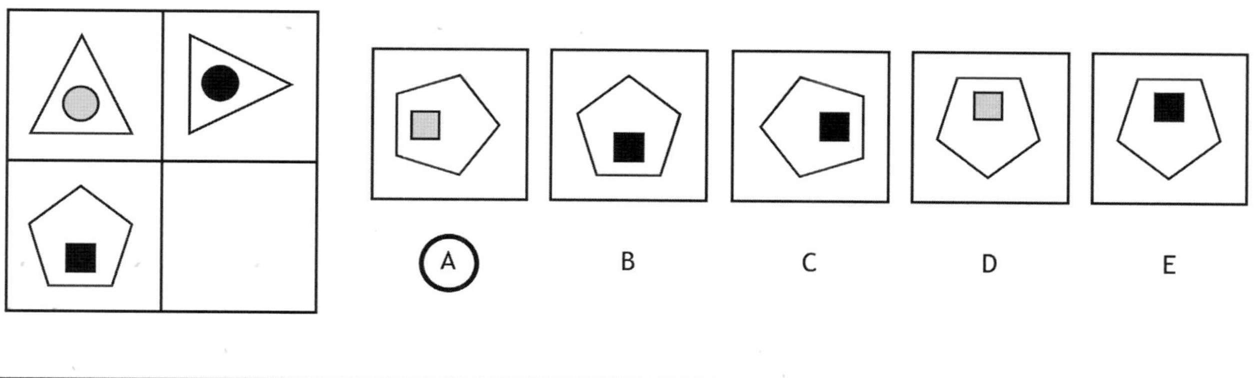

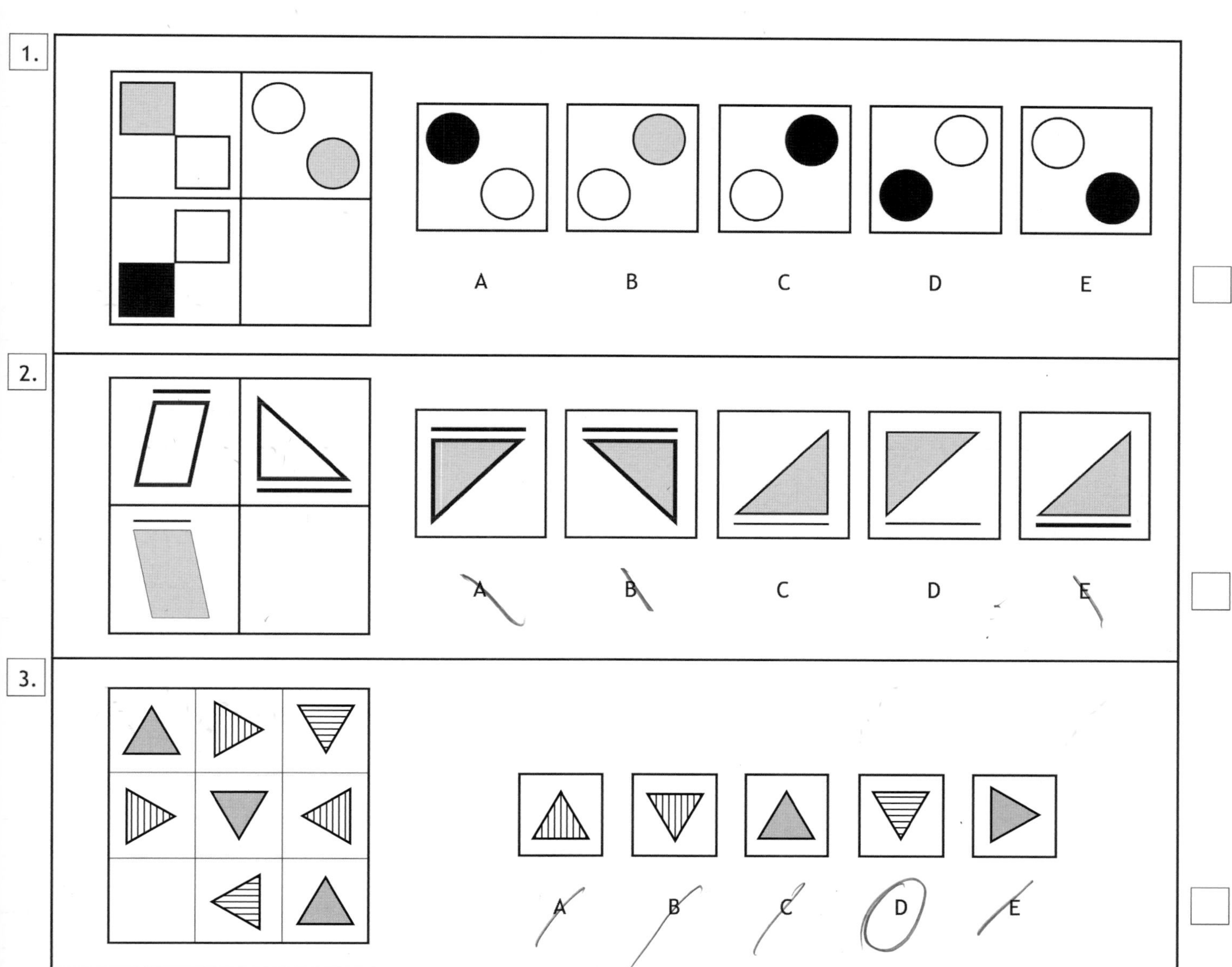

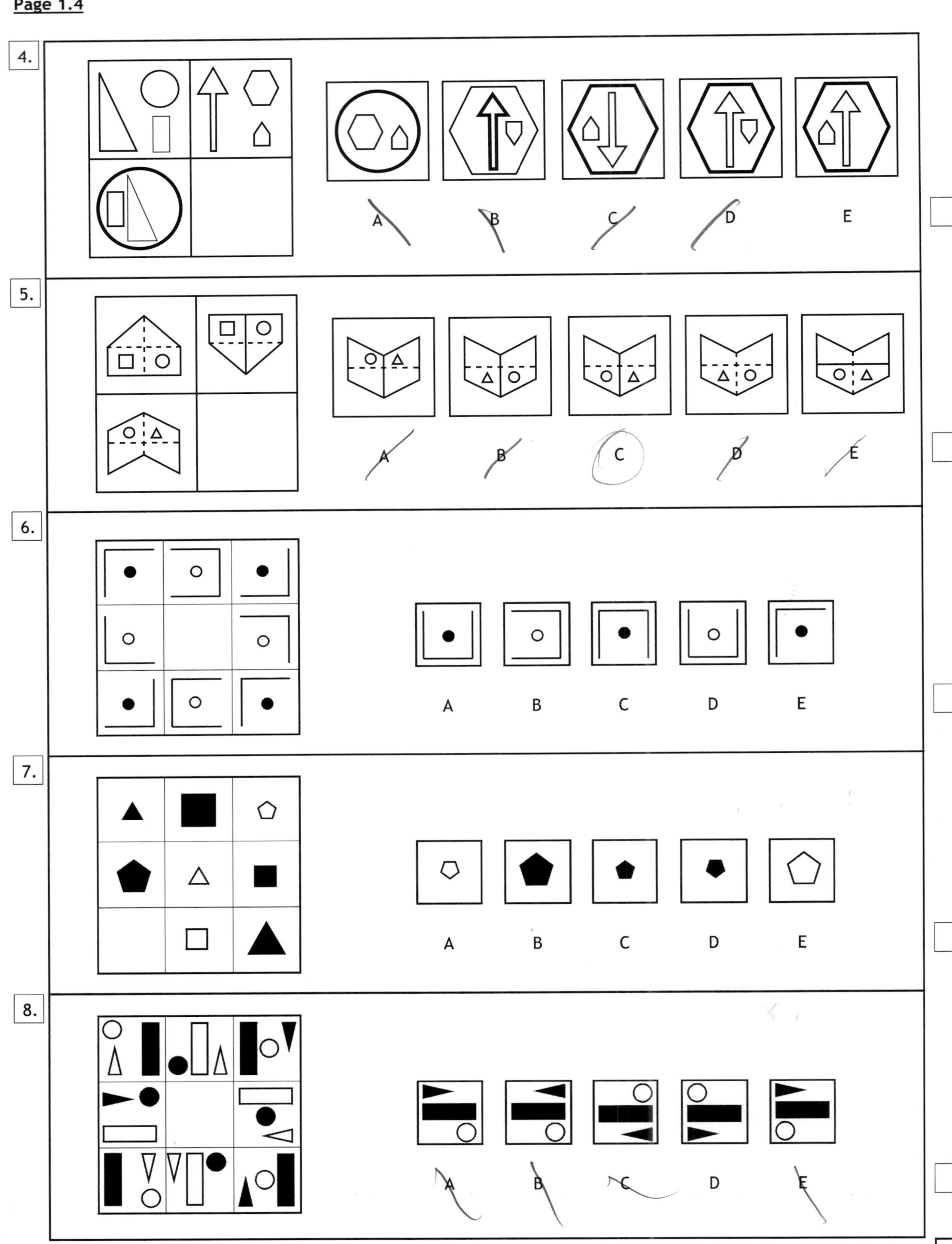
4.
A
B
C
D
E
5.
A
B
C
D
E
6.
A
B
C
D
E
7.
A
B
C
D
E
8.
A
B
C
D
E

Section C

Each of the following questions consists of five figures in a row. They all have something in common, except one. You must find the odd one out.

Choose the figure that you think does not go with the other four and circle the letter on the answer sheet, or mark the appropriate box on the multiple choice answer sheet.

Example:

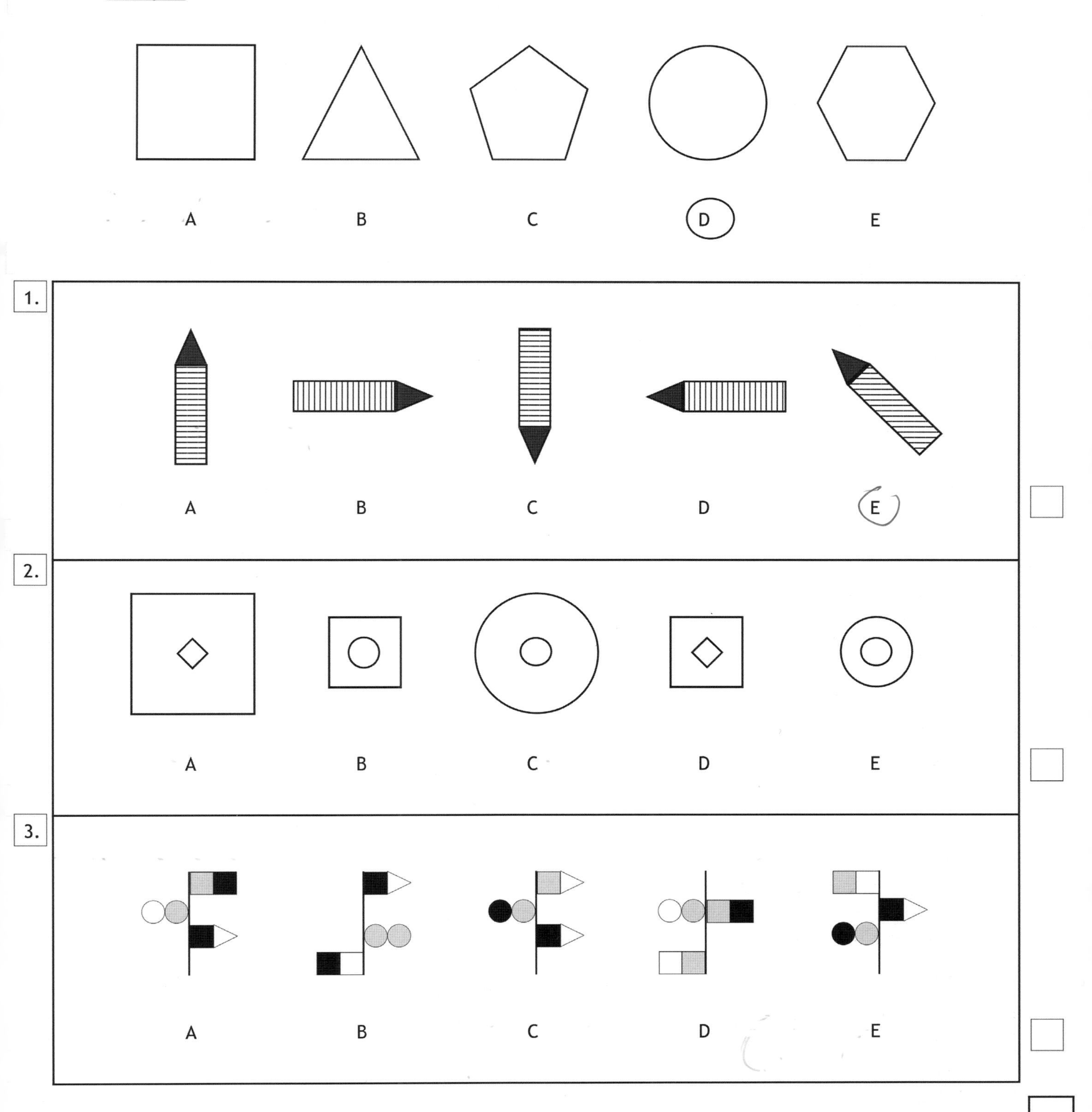

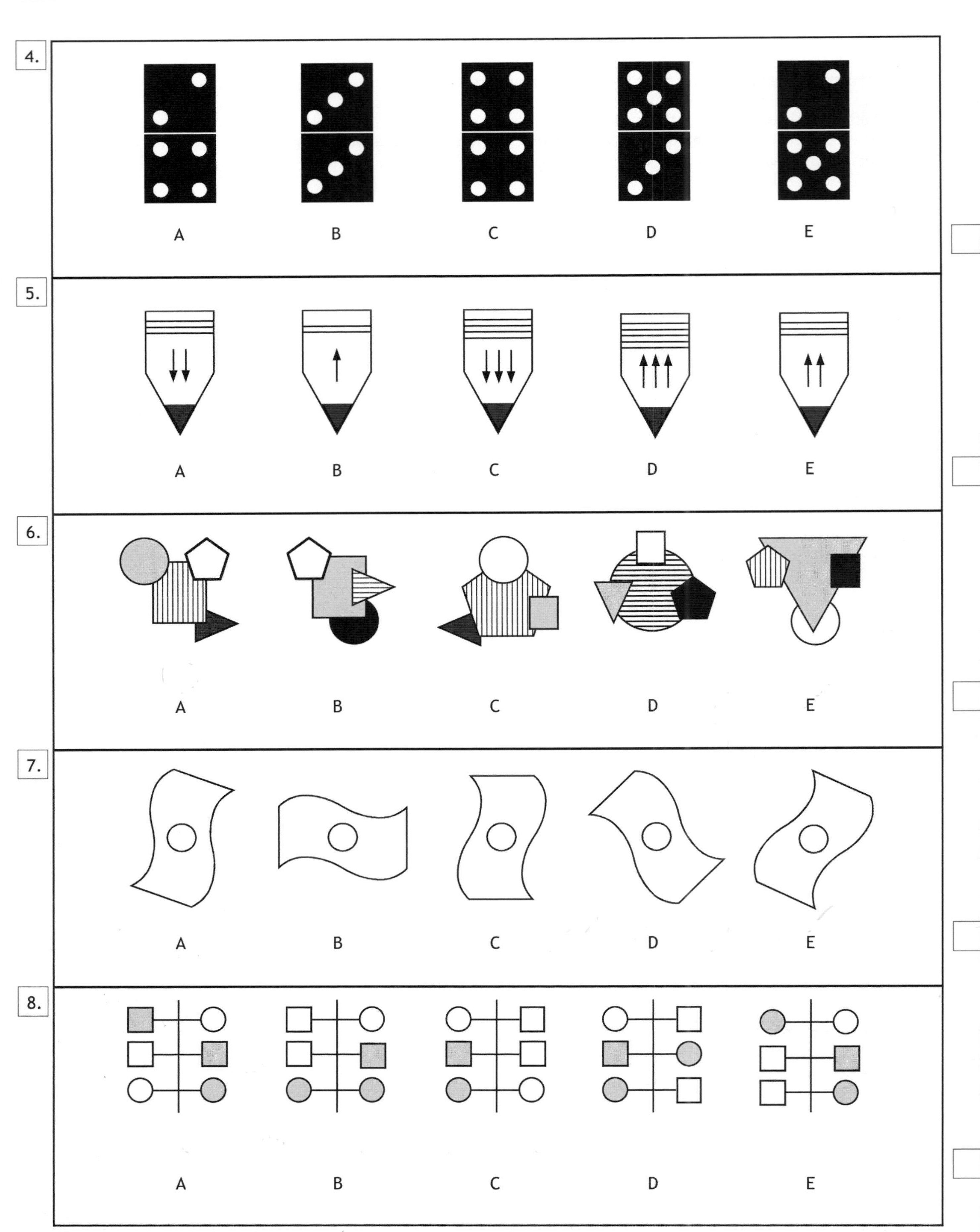
4.
A
B
C
D
E
5.
A
B
C
D
E
6.
A
B
C
D
E
7.
A
B
C
D
E
8.
A
B
C
D
E

Section D

The figures drawn in the boxes on the left hand side of the page have been given letter codes that describe certain aspects of their appearance. Using this information you can find the code for the figure in the box on the right.

Choose the code letters that you think describes the figure in the box on the right hand side and circle the letter on the answer sheet, or mark the appropriate box on the multiple choice answer sheet.

Example:

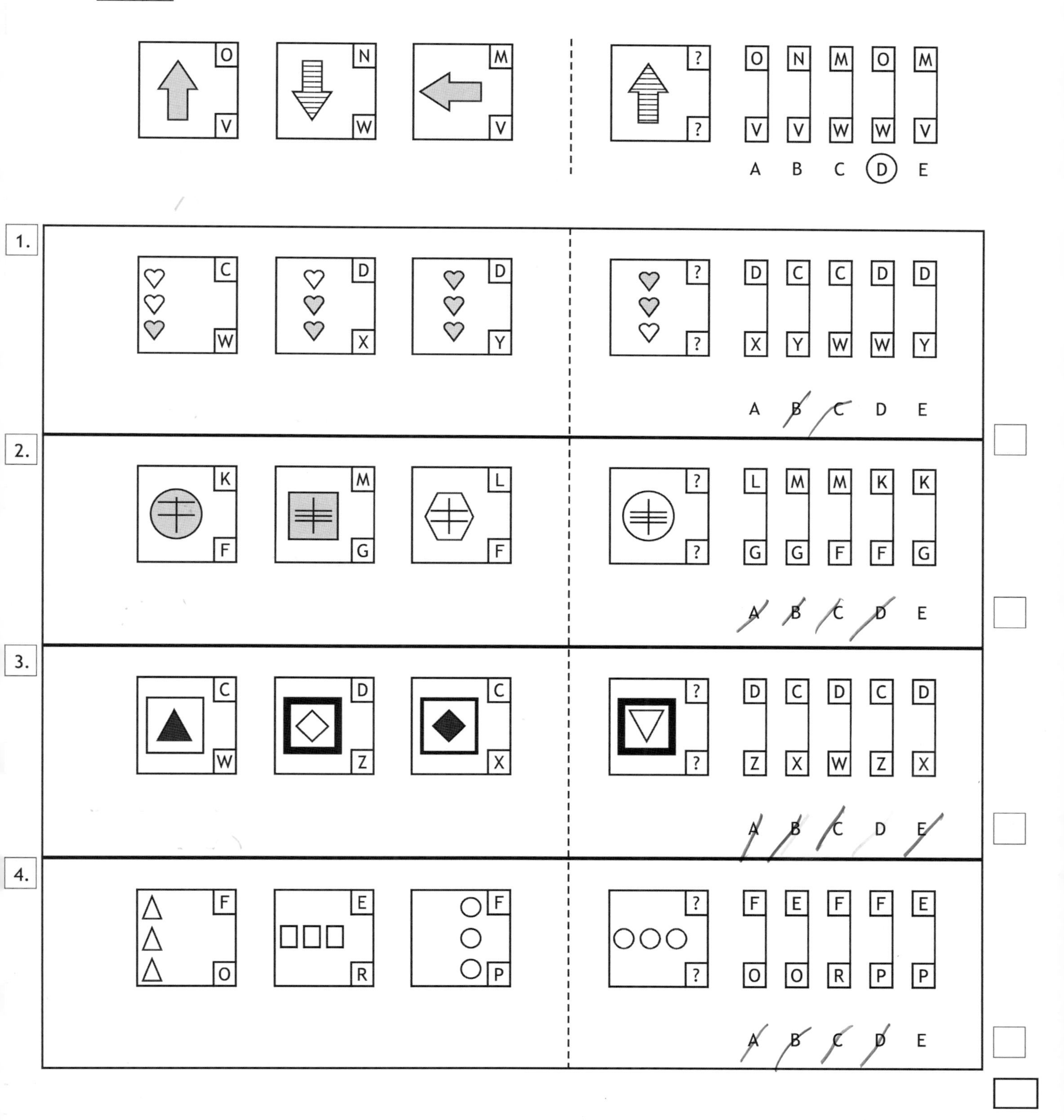

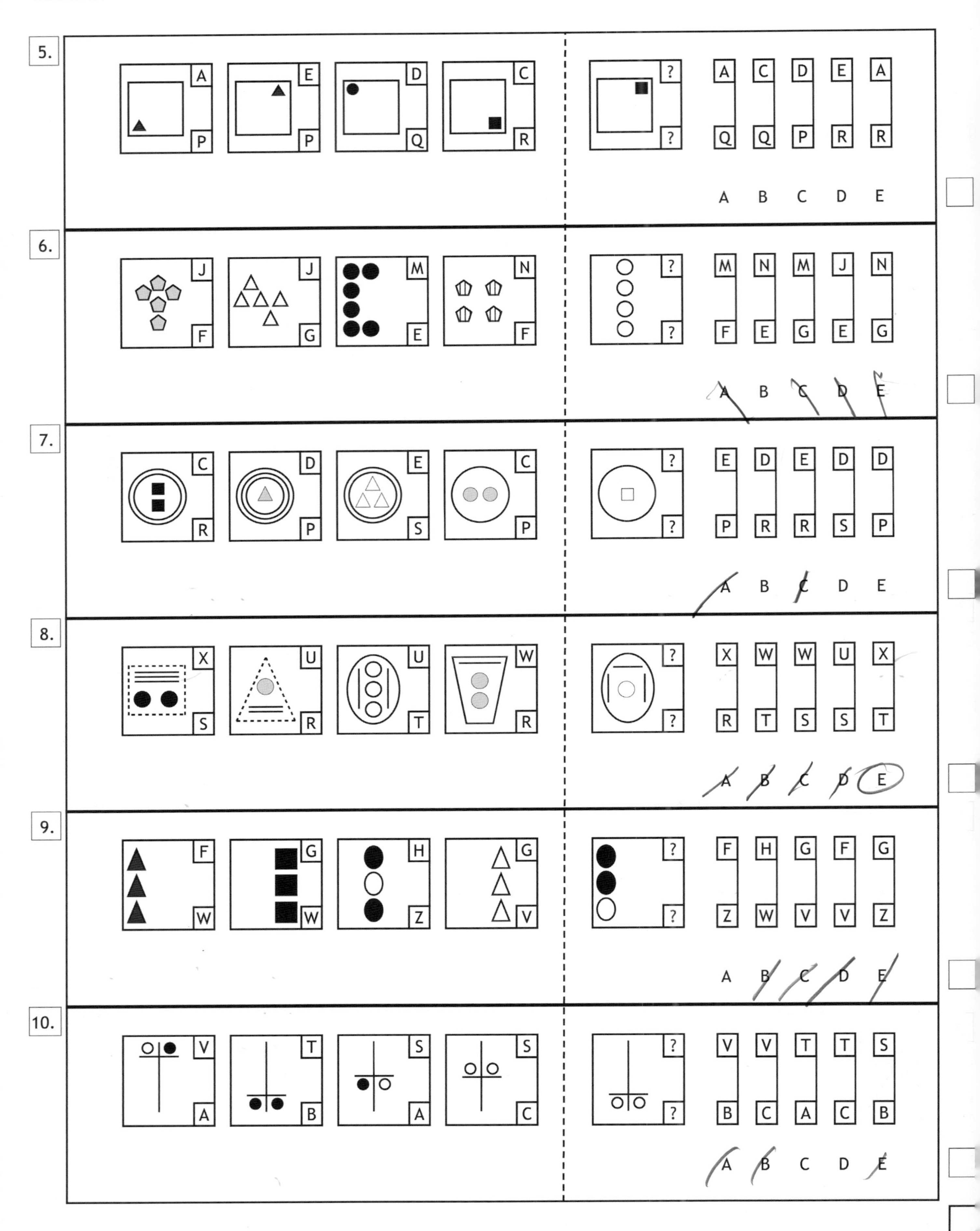
5.
A
P
E
P
D
Q
C
R
?
?
A Q
C Q
D P
E R
A R
A B C D E
6.
J
F
J
G
M
E
N
F
?
?
M F
N E
M G
J E
N G
A B C D E
7.
C
R
D
P
E
S
C
P
?
?
E P
D R
E R
D S
D P
A B C D E
8.
X
S
U
R
U
T
W
R
?
?
X R
W T
W S
U S
X T
A B C D E
9.
F
W
G
W
H
Z
G
V
?
?
F Z
H W
G V
F V
G Z
A B C D E
10.
V
A
T
B
S
A
S
C
?
?
V B
V C
T A
T C
S B
A B C D E

Practice Paper 2.

There are 35 questions in four sections on this paper. You have 30 minutes to complete this test.

Circle your answers carefully on the answer sheet or place a mark in the multiple choice answer box on the separate sheet.

Section A

On the left of each question are two figures connected by an arrow. You must work out how the second figure is related to the first. Now look at the third figure. Which of the five other figures that follow is related to the third in the same way that the second is to the first?

Choose the shape that you think goes with the third shape and circle the letter on the answer sheet, or mark the appropriate box on the multiple choice answer sheet.

Example:

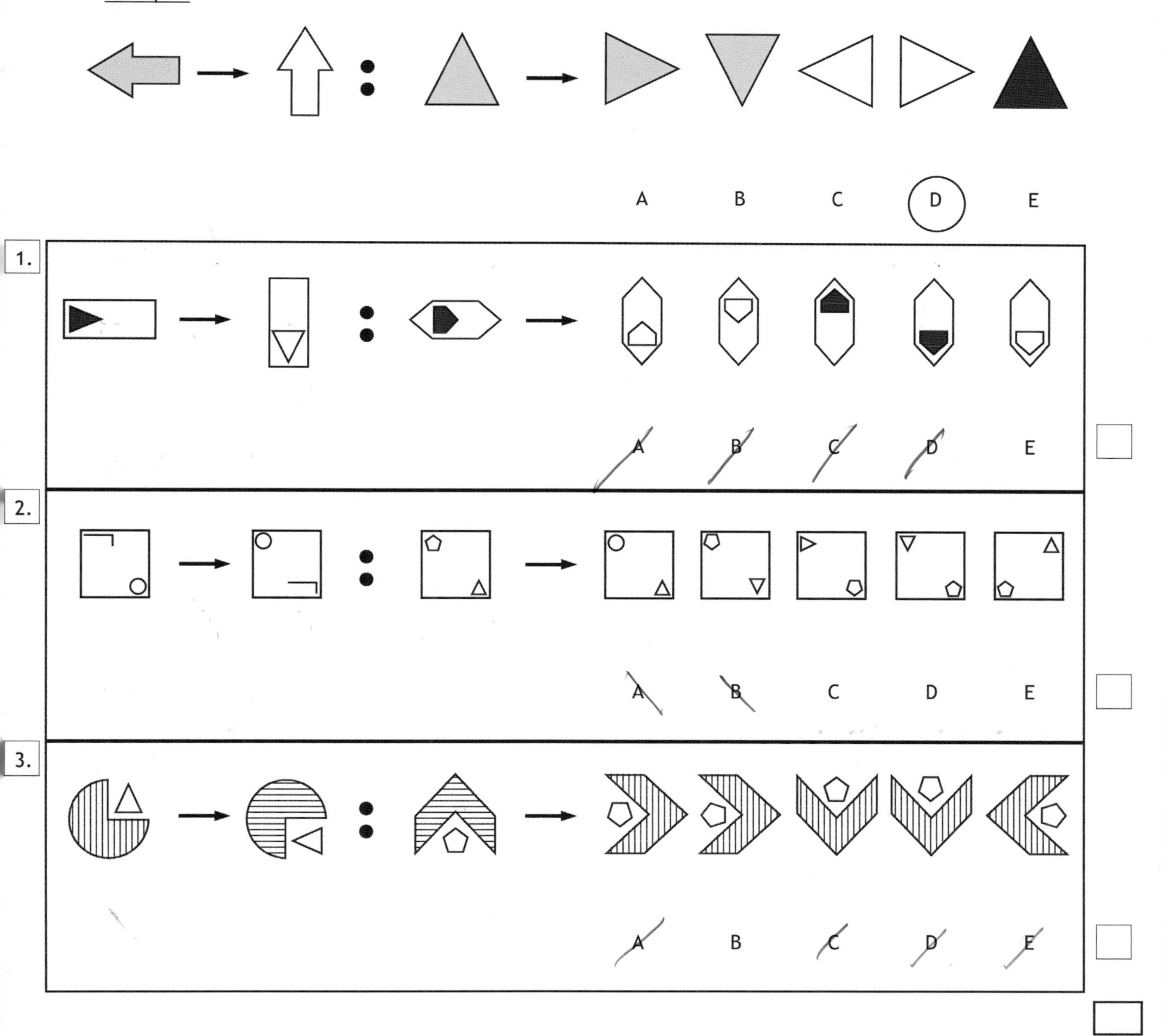

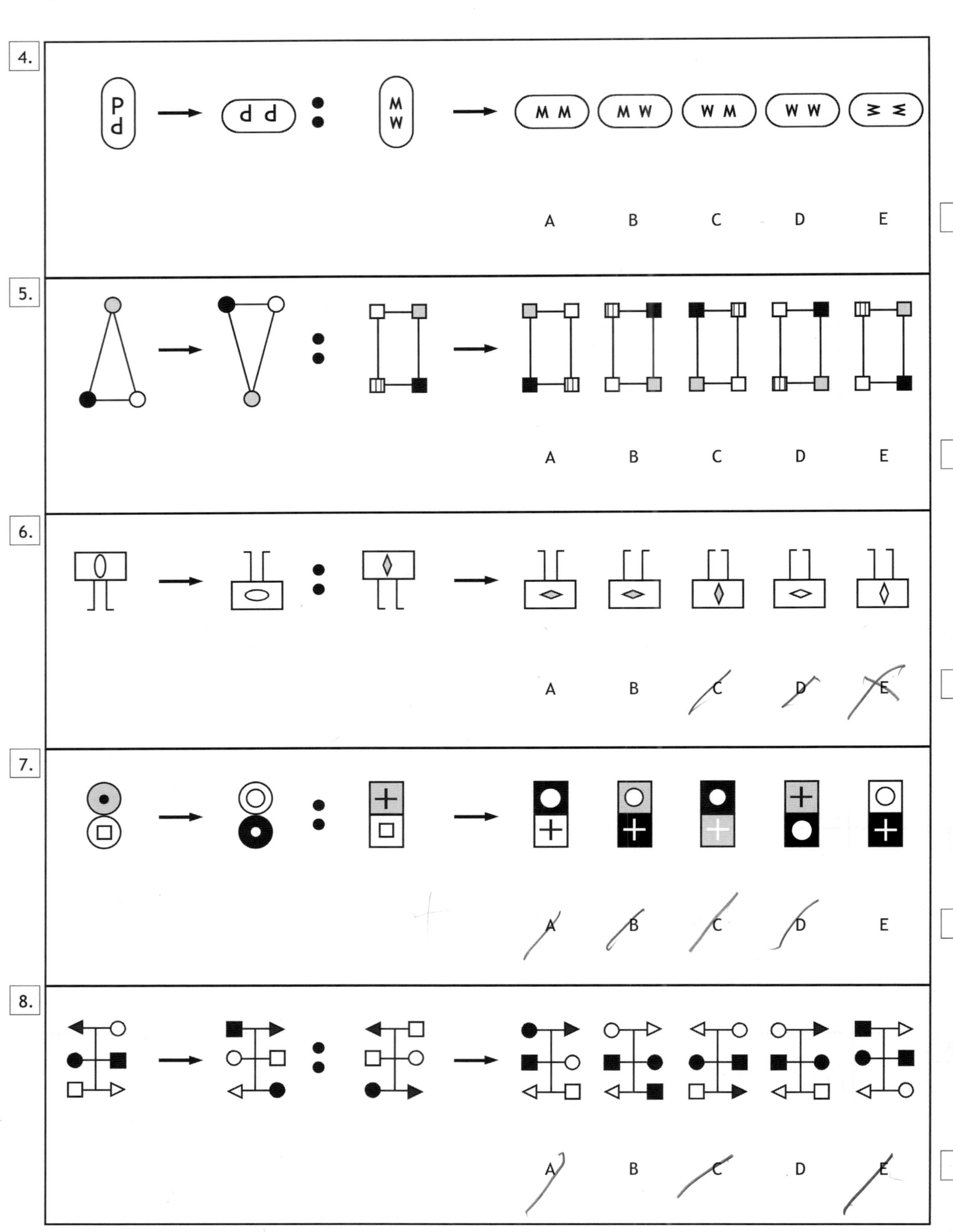
4.
P
d
d p
M
W
M M
M W
W M
W W
A
B
C
D
E
5.
A
B
C
D
E
6.
A
B
C
D
E
7.
A
B
C
D
E
8.
A
B
C
D
E

Section B

Each of the following questions consists of five shapes in a row. They all have something in common, except one. You must find the odd one out.

Choose the shape that you think does not go with the other four and circle the letter on the answer sheet, or mark the appropriate box on the multiple choice answer sheet.

Example:

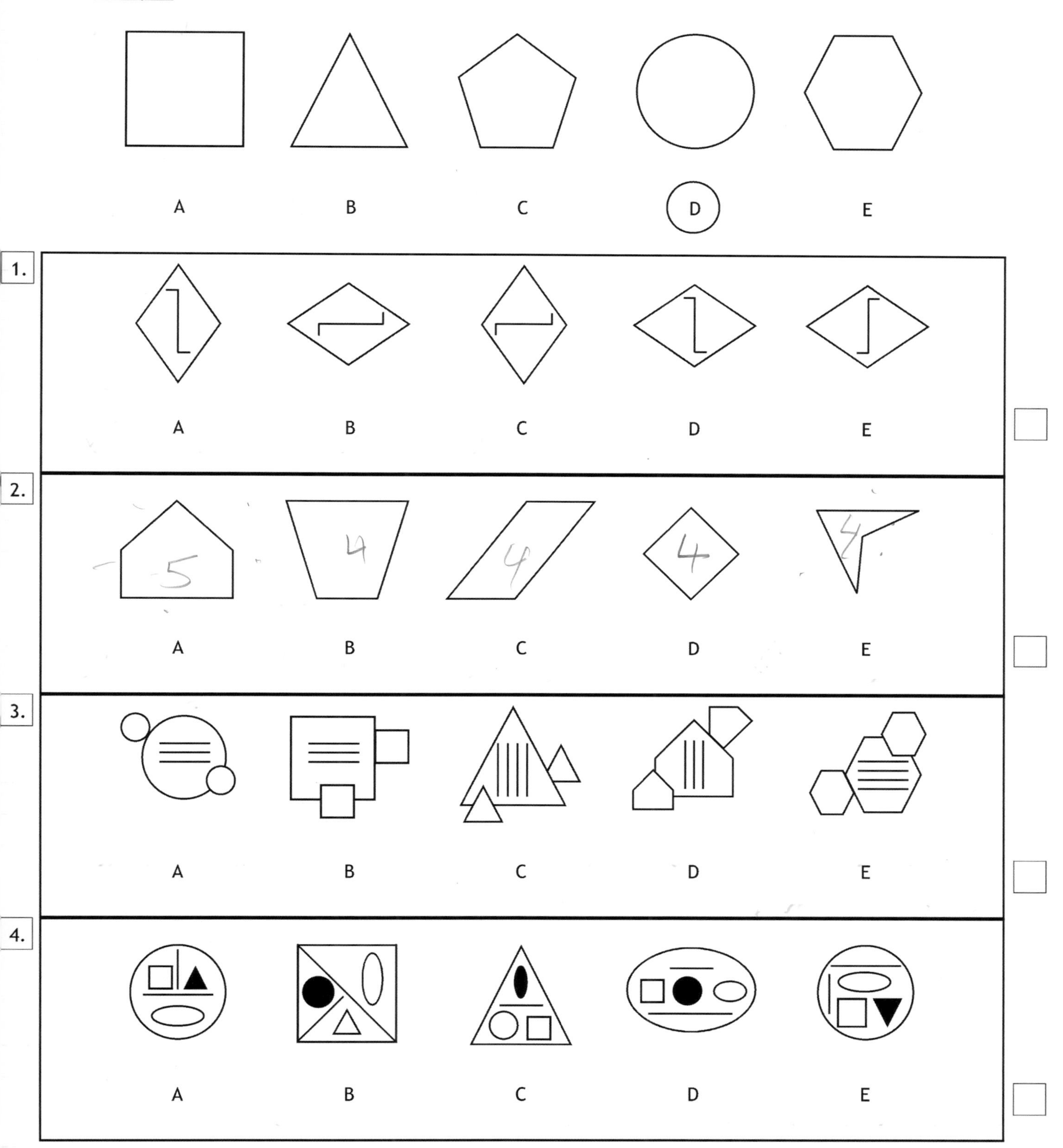

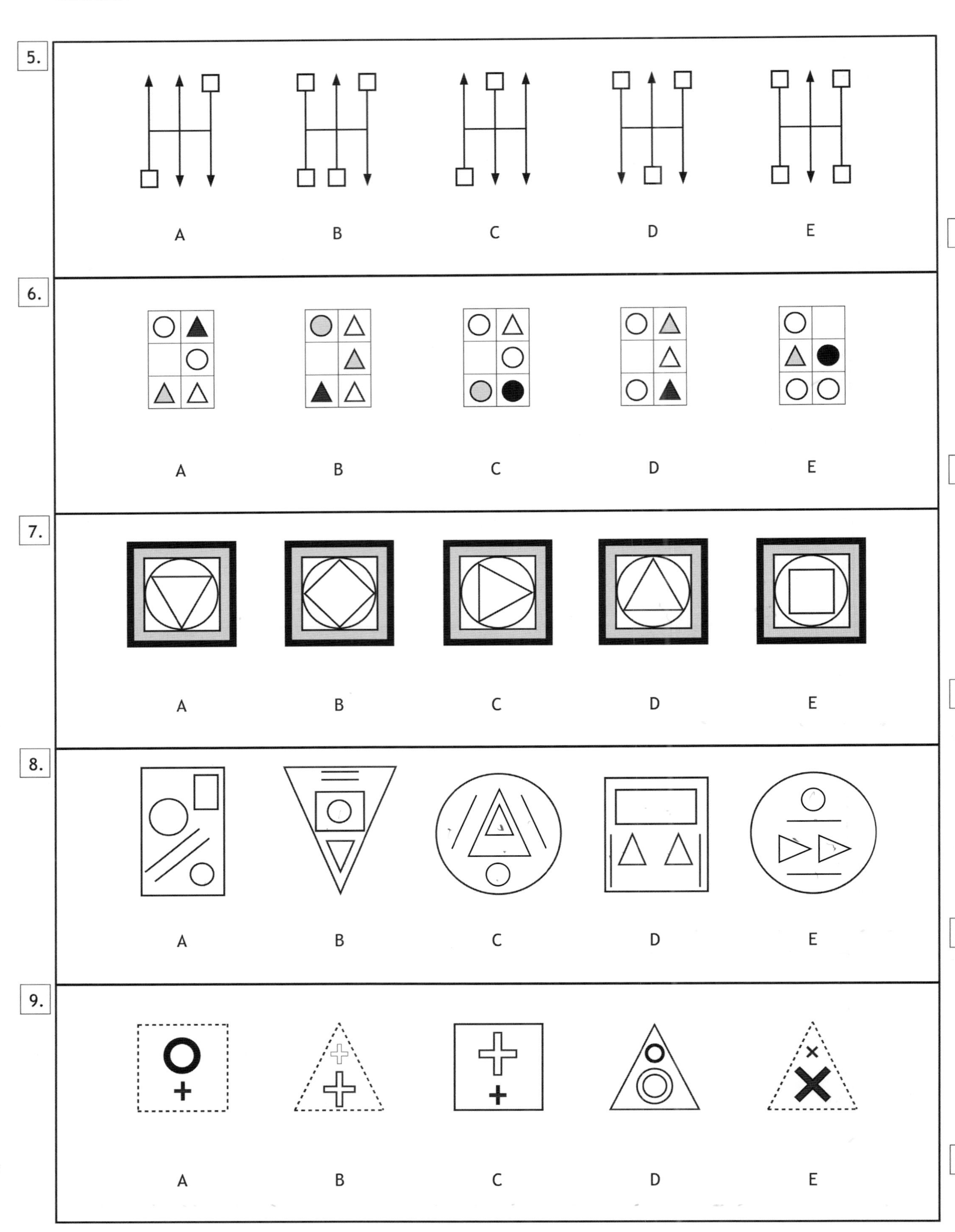
5.
A
B
C
D
E
6.
A
B
C
D
E
7.
A
B
C
D
E
8.
A
B
C
D
E
9.
A
B
C
D
E

Section C

The shapes drawn on the left hand side of the page have been given letter codes that describe certain aspects of their appearance. Using this information you can find the code for the single shape.

Choose the code that you think describes the single shape and circle the letter on the answer sheet, or mark the appropriate box on the multiple choice answer sheet.

Example:

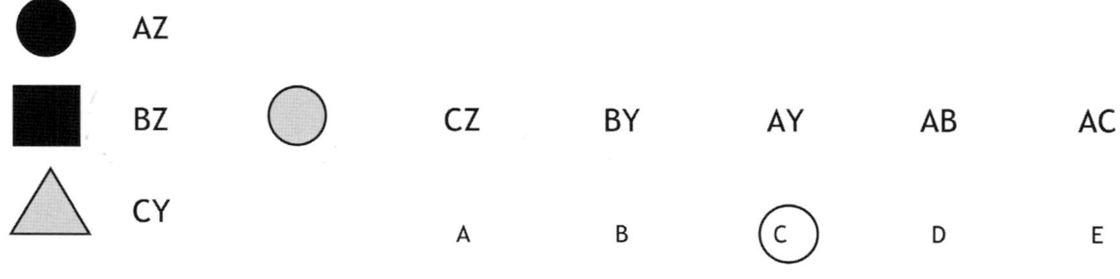

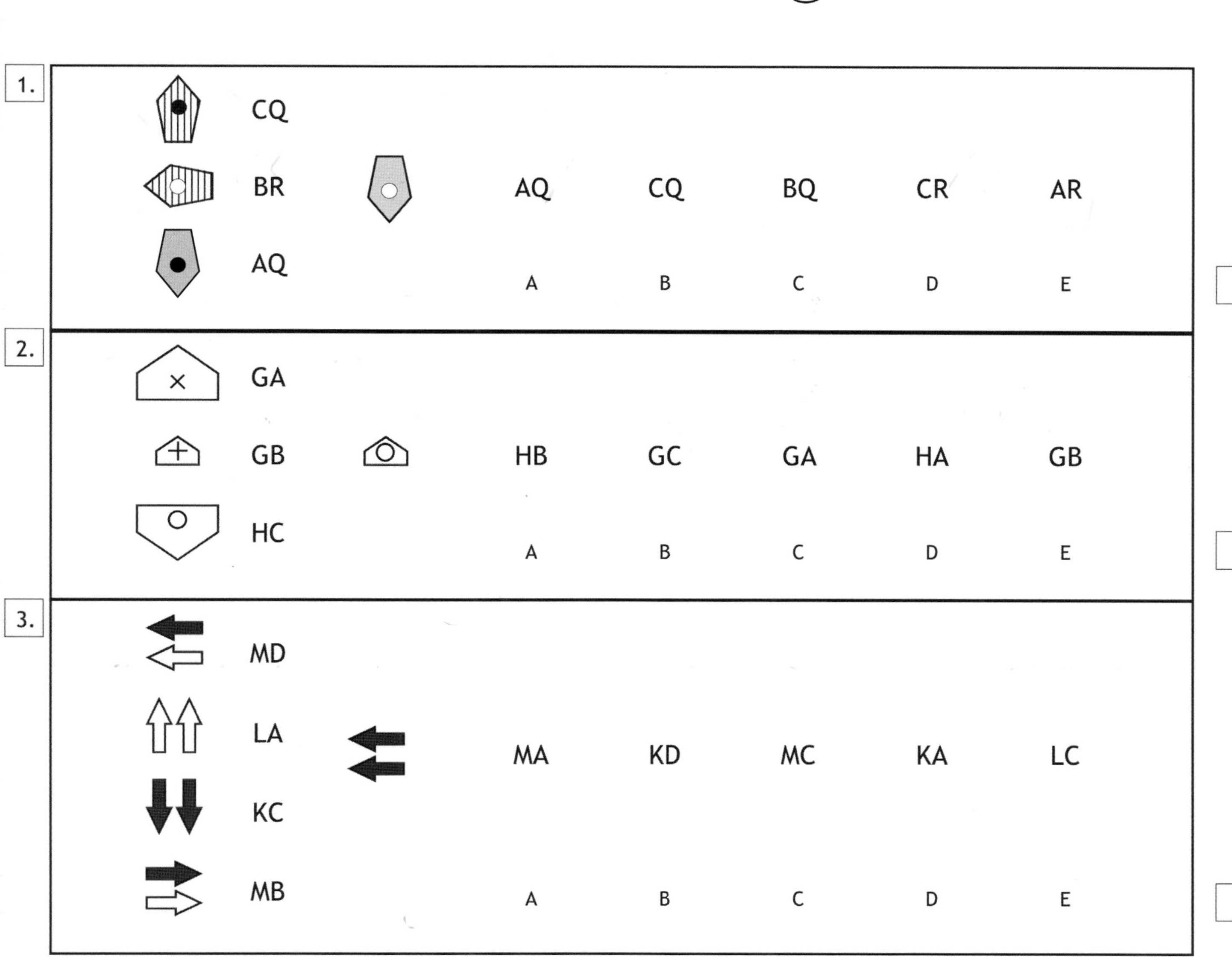

4.

VDQ

WAR

VPR

WDR	VDQ	WPQ	VAR	VPR
A	B	C	D	E

5.

MH

NG

OH

NH	NG	MG	OG	MH
A	B	C	D	E

6.

HFC

KFB

JGB

HGA

KGC	HFA	JGC	JFA	HGC
A	B	C	D	E

7.

SC

TE

SD

VF

VC	TC	SE	VD	TD
A	B	C	D	E

8.

DJ

FK

EL

GJ

EJ	FJ	EK	GL	DJ
A	B	C	D	E

Section D

On the left hand side of the page there are two shapes that are similar. On the right hand side there are five other shapes.

You must choose one shape of the five that you is most alike to the first two and circle its letter on the answer sheet, or mark the appropriate box on the multiple choice answer sheet.

Example:

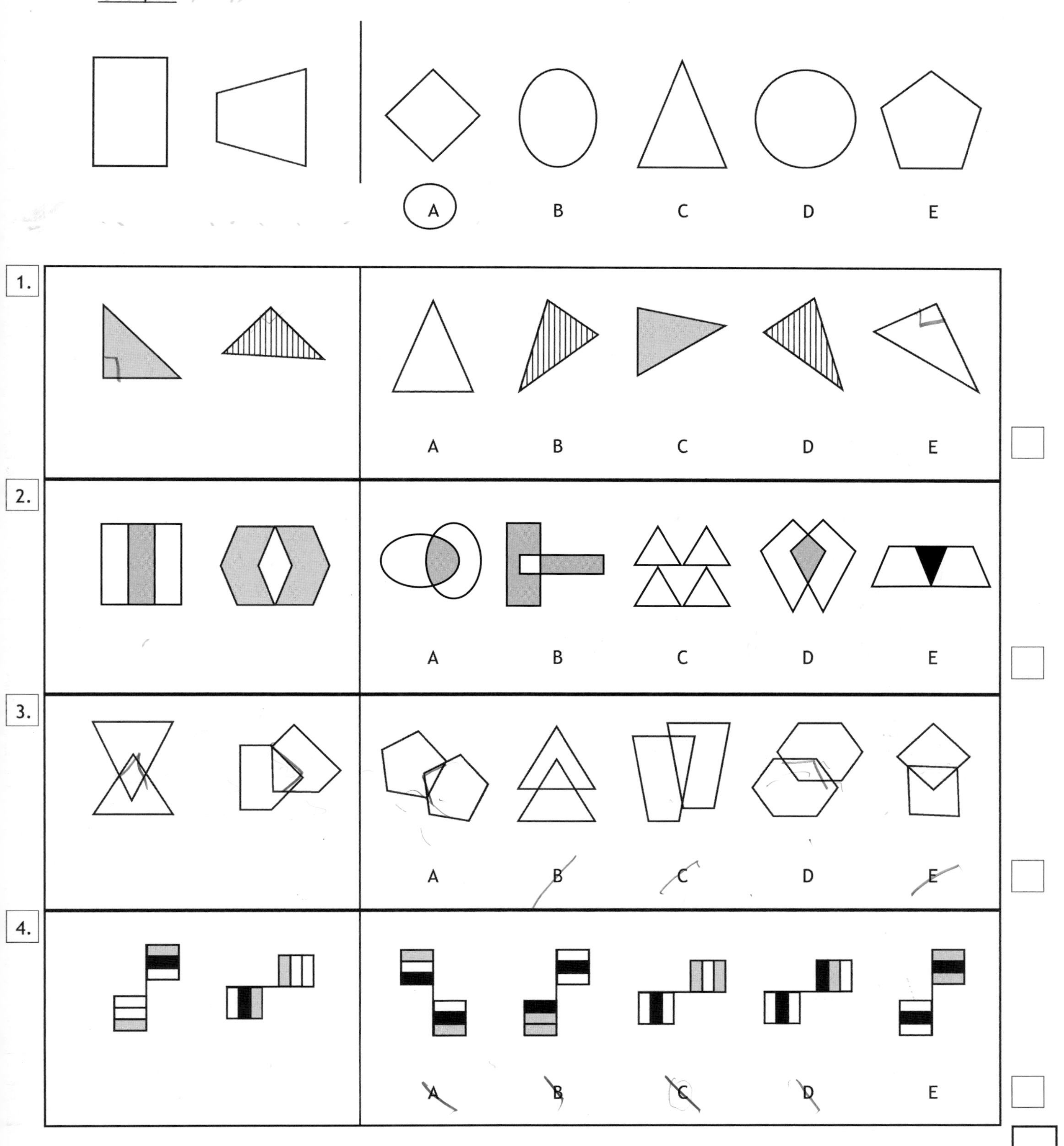

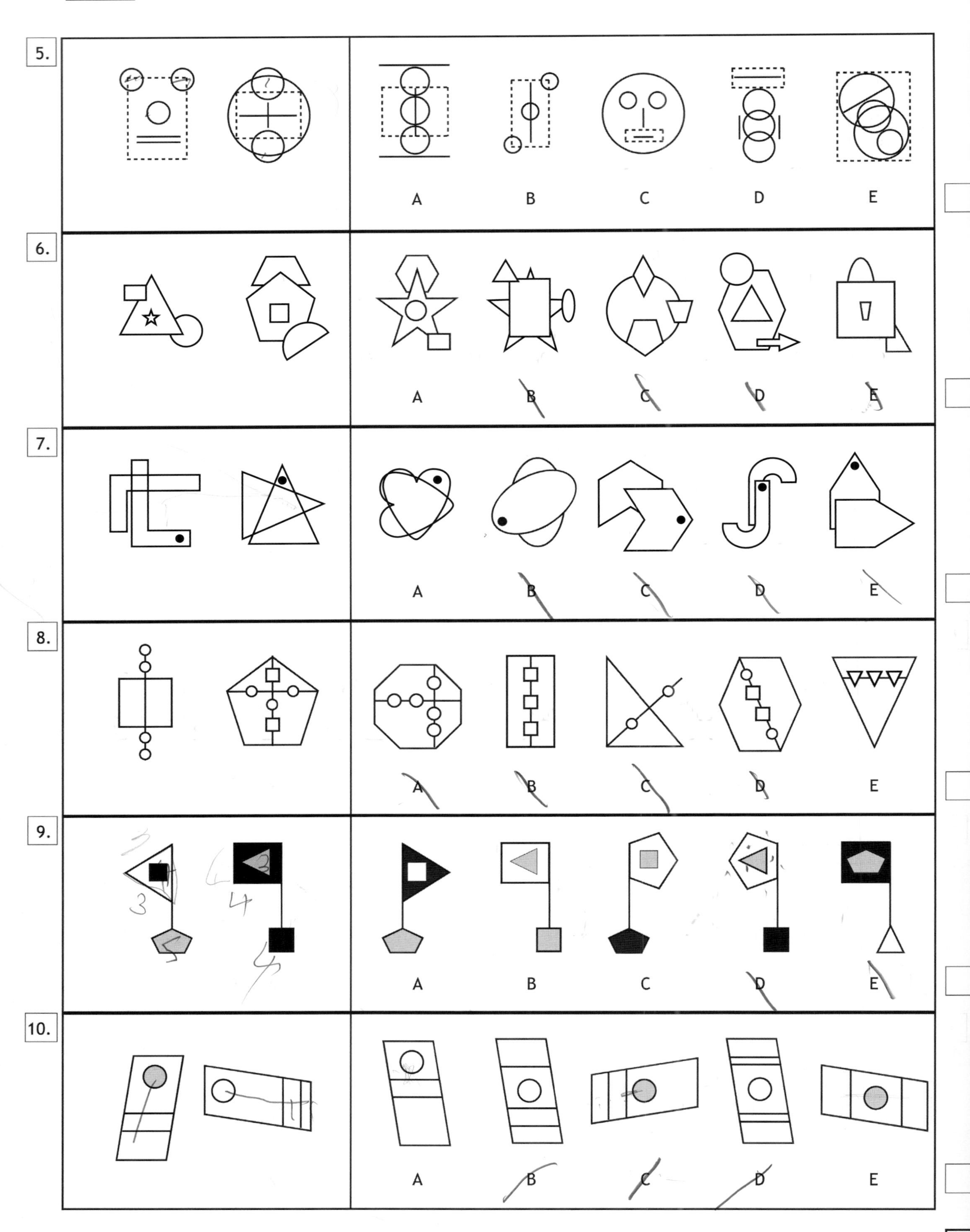
5.
A
B
C
D
E
6.
A
B
C
D
E
7.
A
B
C
D
E
8.
A
B
C
D
E
9.
A
B
C
D
E
10.
A
B
C
D
E

Practice Paper 3.

There are 35 questions in four sections on this paper. You have 30 minutes to complete this test.

Circle your answers carefully on the answer sheet or place a mark in the multiple choice answer box on the separate sheet.

Section A

The shapes drawn in the boxes on the left hand side of the page have been given letter codes that describe certain aspects of their appearance. Using this information you can find the code for the shape in the box on the right.

Choose the code letters that you think describes the shape in the box on the right hand side and circle the letter on the answer sheet, or mark the appropriate box on the multiple choice answer sheet.

Example:

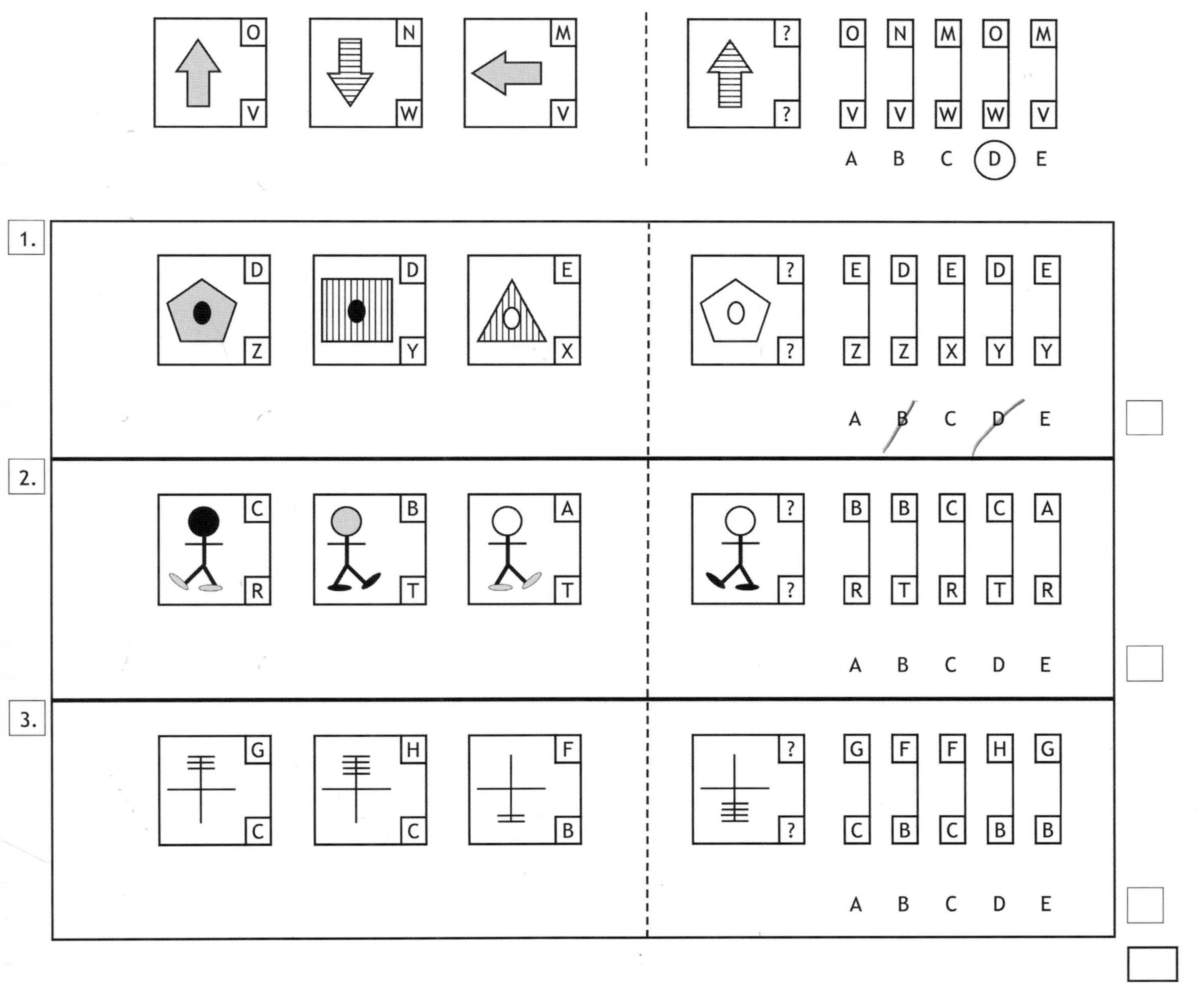

Page 3.2

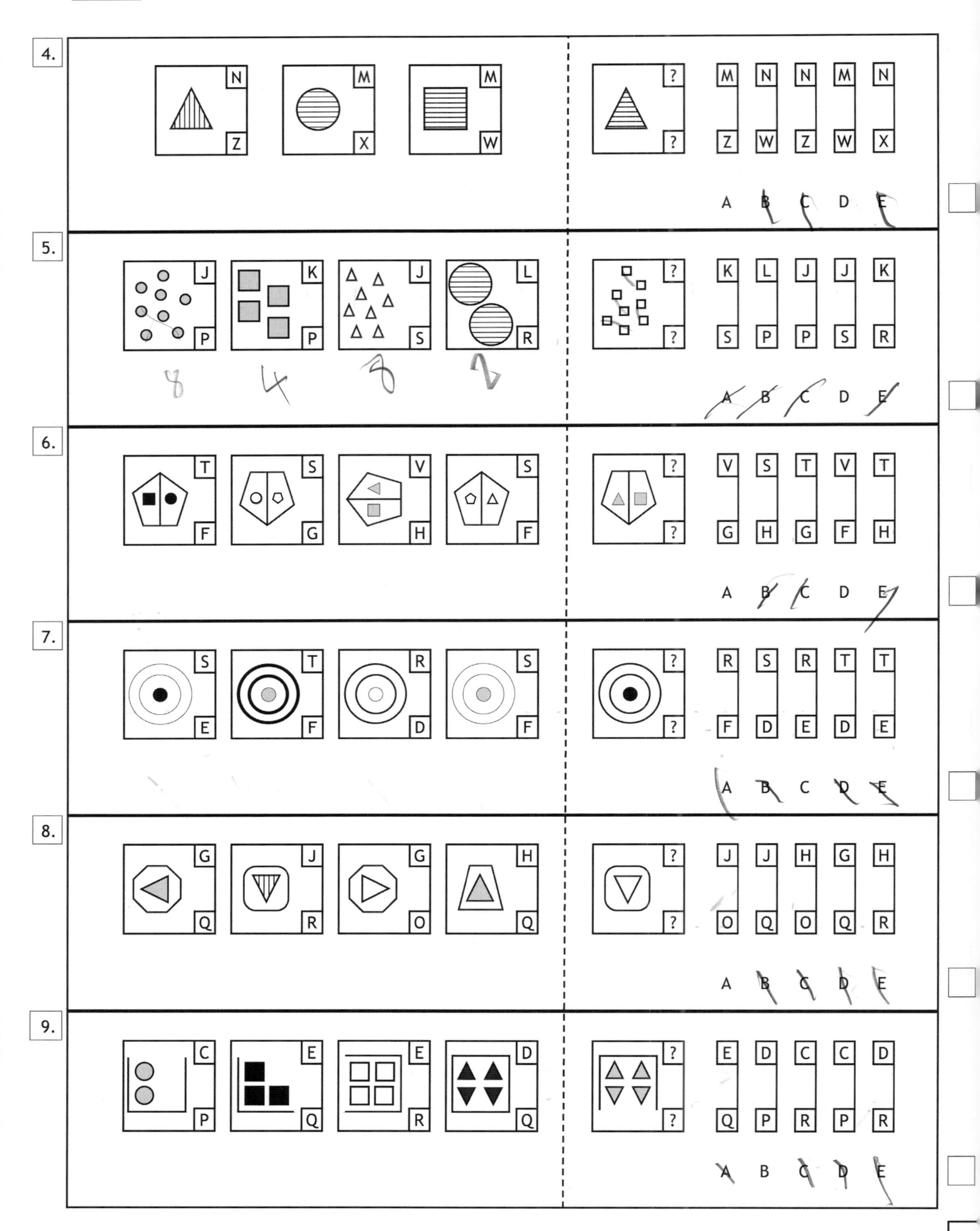

4.
N
Z
M
X
M
W
?
?
M Z
N W
N Z
M W
N X
A B C D E
5.
J
P
K
P
J
S
L
R
?
?
K S
L P
J P
J S
K R
A B C D E
6.
T
F
S
G
V
H
S
F
?
?
V G
S H
T G
V F
T H
A B C D E
7.
S
E
T
F
R
D
S
F
?
?
R F
S D
R E
T D
T E
A B C D E
8.
G
Q
J
R
G
O
H
Q
?
?
J O
J Q
H O
G Q
H R
A B C D E
9.
C
P
E
Q
E
R
D
Q
?
?
E Q
D P
C R
C P
D R
A B C D E

Section B

There are figures drawn in three sections of the large square on the left hand side of the page. One of the small squares is empty. This square can be filled by only one of the five boxes on the right.

Choose the box that you think will best complete the large square and circle the letter on the answer sheet, or mark the appropriate box on the multiple choice answer sheet.

Example:

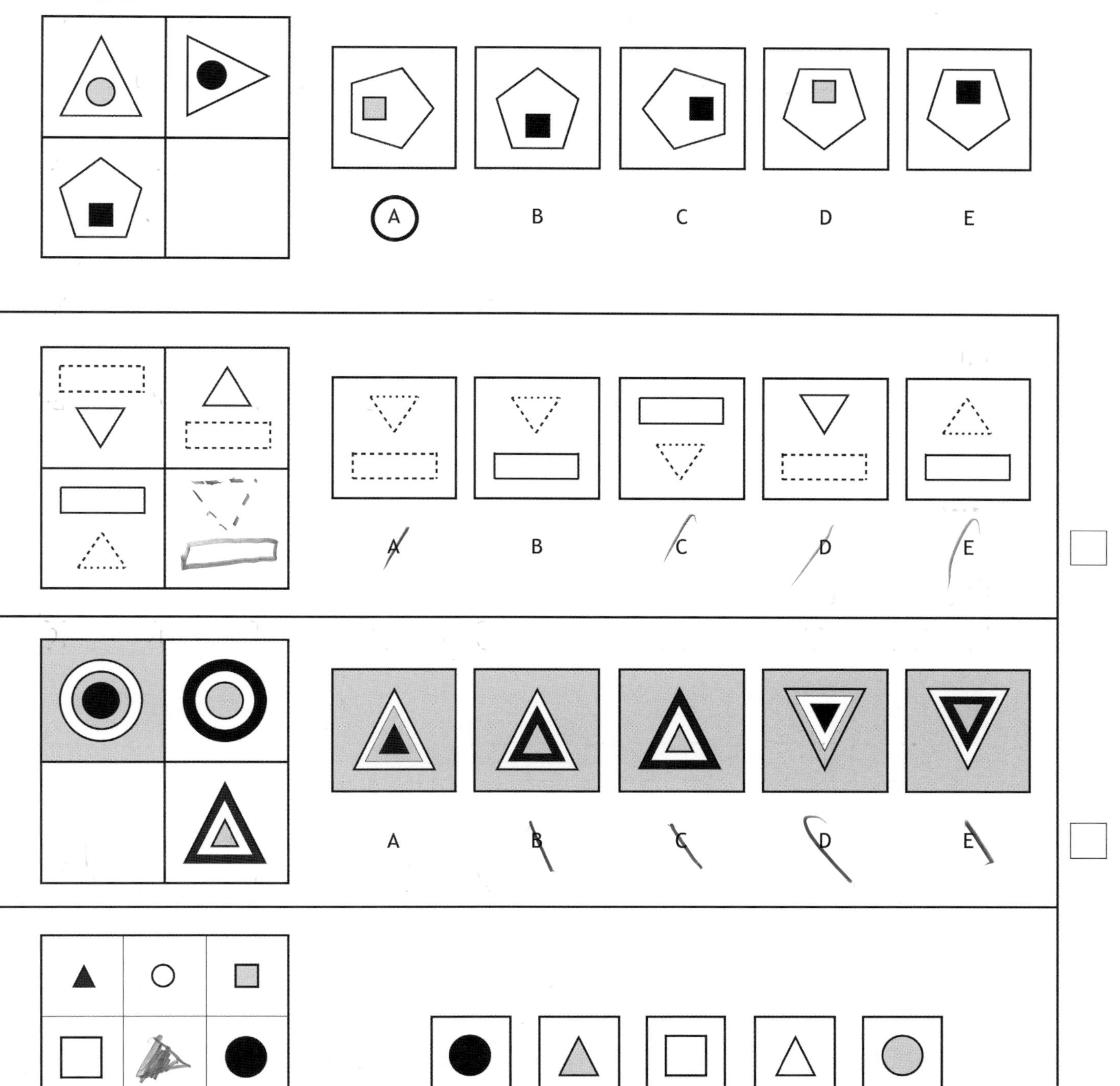

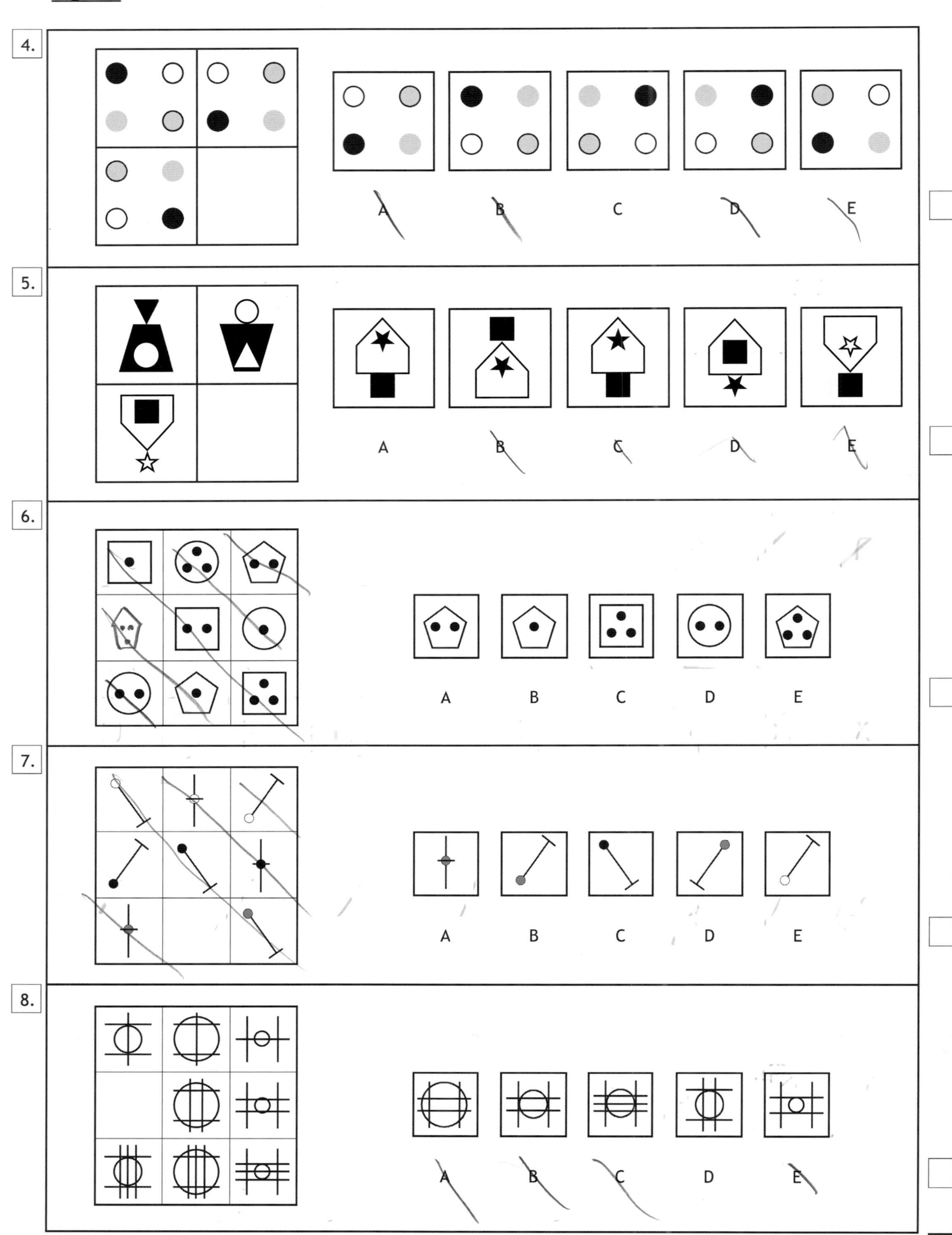

4.
A
B
C
D
E
5.
A
B
C
D
E
6.
A
B
C
D
E
7.
A
B
C
D
E
8.
A
B
C
D
E

Section C

On the left of the page is a sequence of figures in five boxes. One of the boxes is empty. This box can be filled by only one of the figures in the five boxes on the right.

Choose the figure that you think will best complete the sequence and circle the letter on the answer sheet, or mark the appropriate box on the multiple choice answer sheet.

Example:

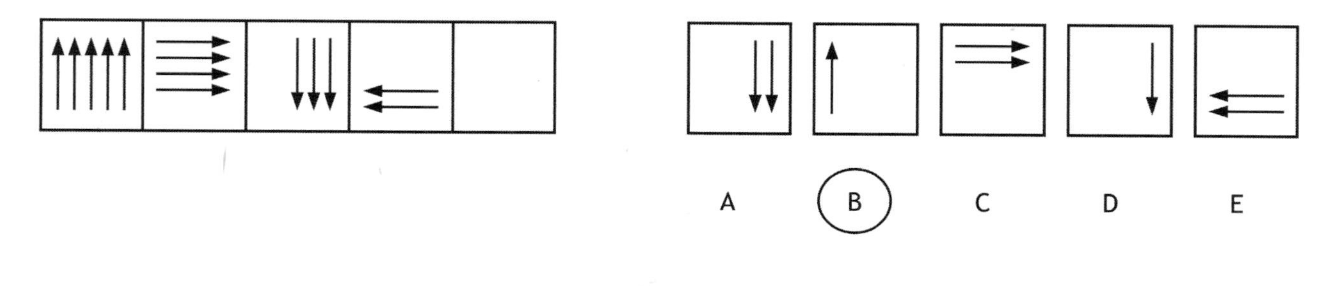

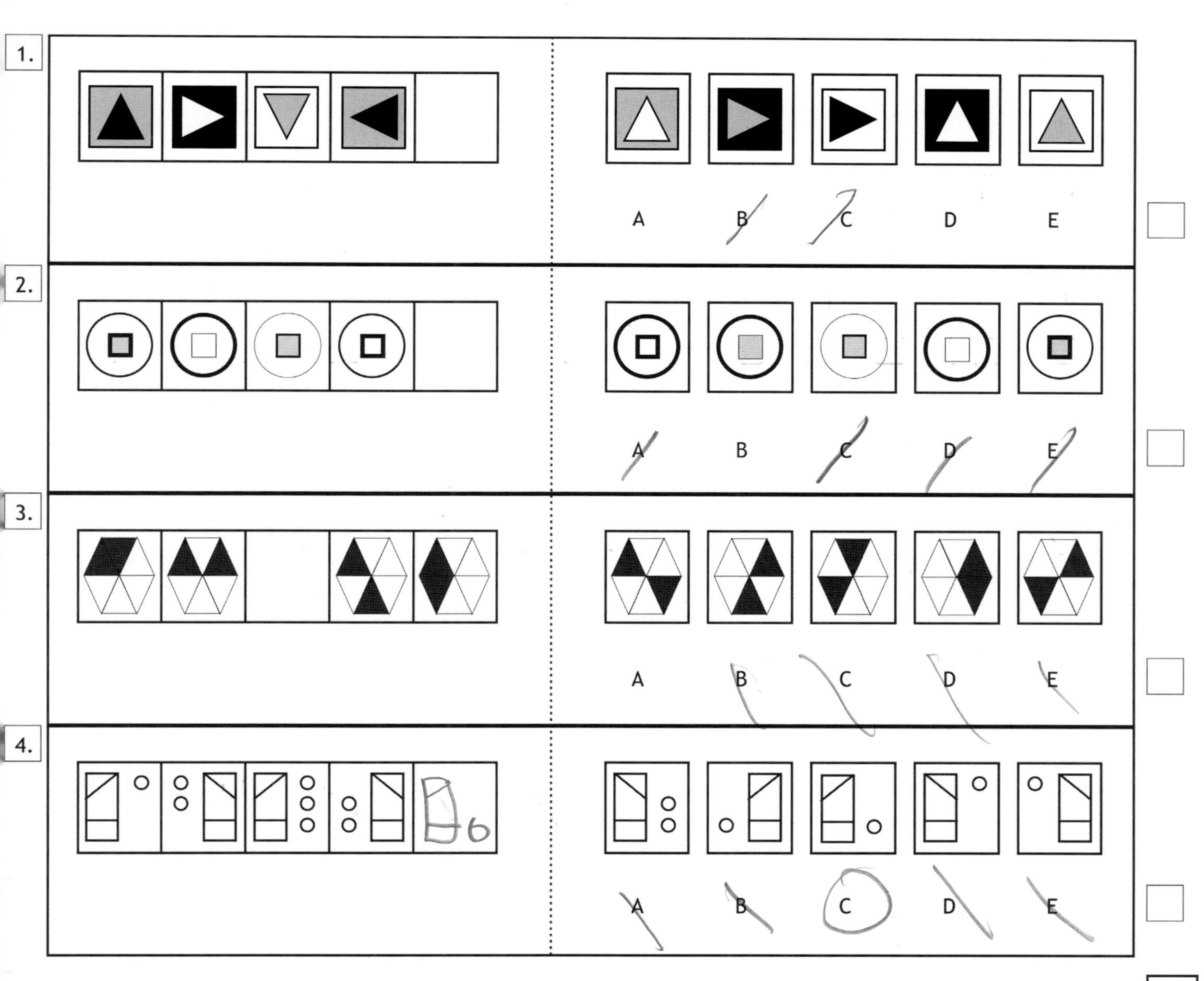

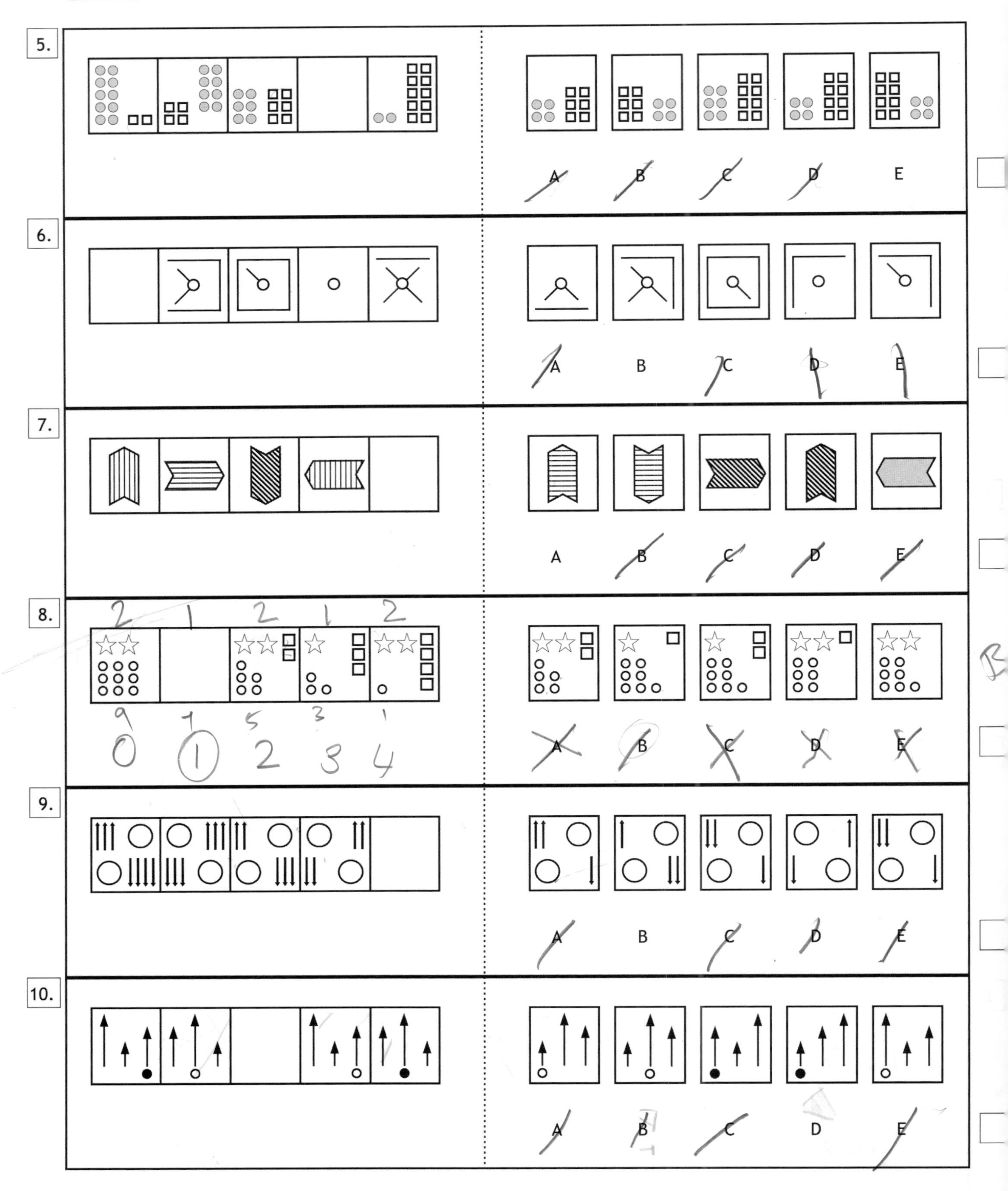
5.
A
B
C
D
E
6.
A
B
C
D
E
7.
A
B
C
D
E
8.
A
B
C
D
E
9.
A
B
C
D
E
10.
A
B
C
D
E

Section D

Each of the following questions consists of five shapes in a row. They all have something in common, except one. You must find the odd one out.

Choose the shape that you think does not go with the other four and circle the letter on the answer sheet, or mark the appropriate box on the multiple choice answer sheet.

Example:

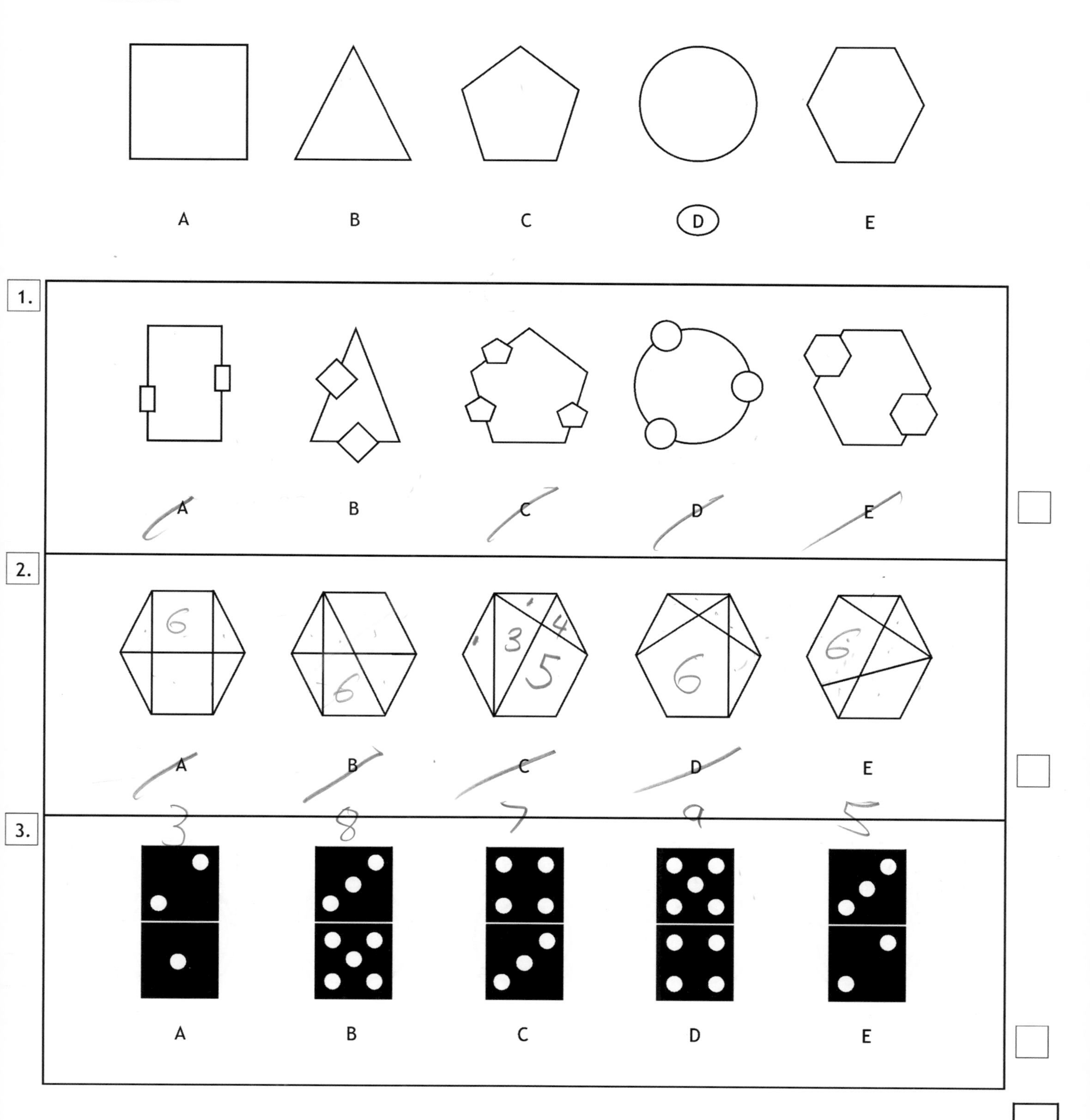

Page 3.8

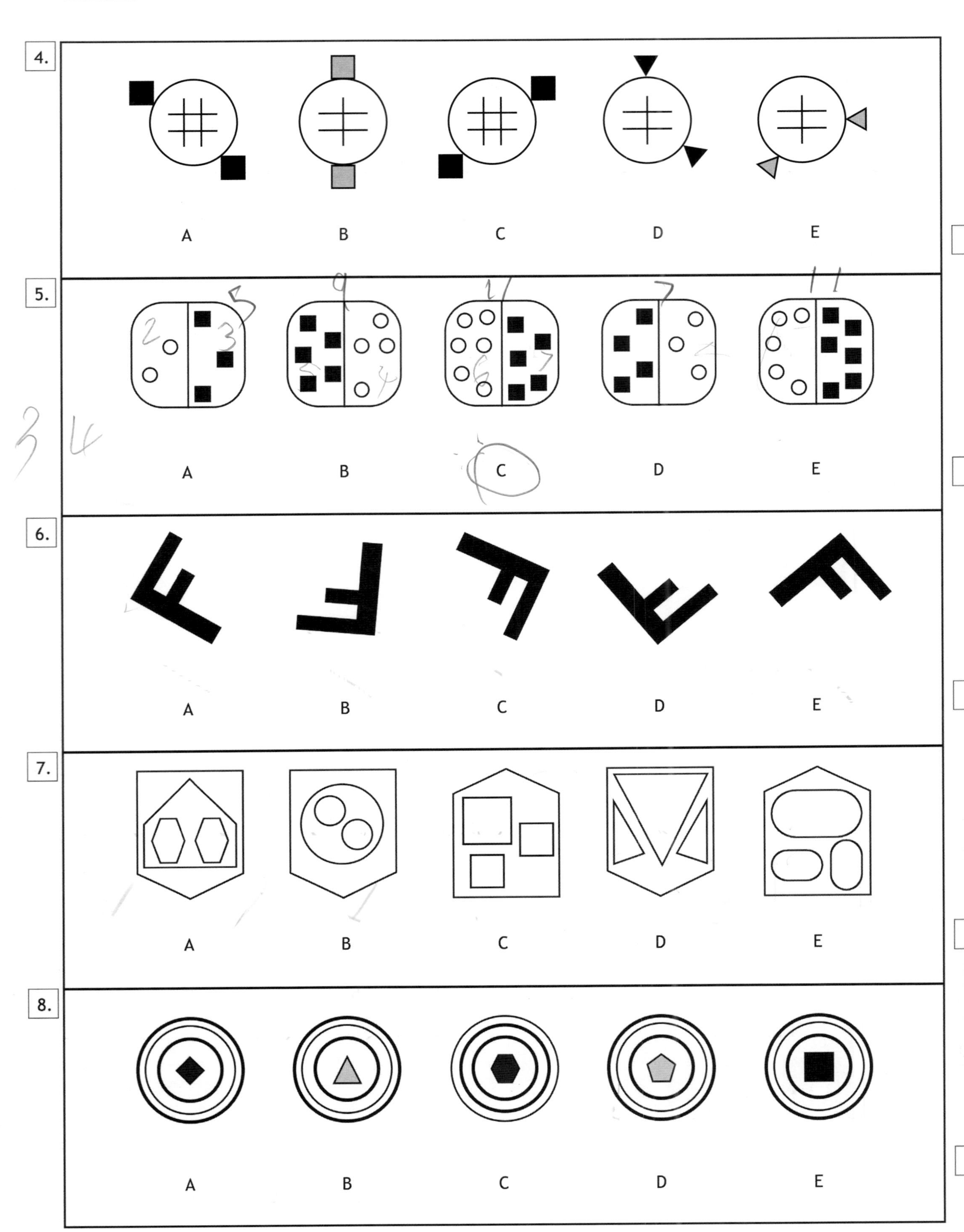

Practice Paper 4.

There are 35 questions in four sections on this paper. You have 30 minutes to complete this test.

Circle your answers carefully on the answer sheet or place a mark in the multiple choice answer box on the separate sheet.

Section A

On the left of each question are two figures connected by an arrow. You must work out how the second figure is related to the first. Now look at the third figure. Which of the five other figures that follow is related to the third in the same way that the second is to the first?

Choose the shape that you think goes with the third shape and circle the letter on the answer sheet, or mark the appropriate box on the multiple choice answer sheet.

Example:

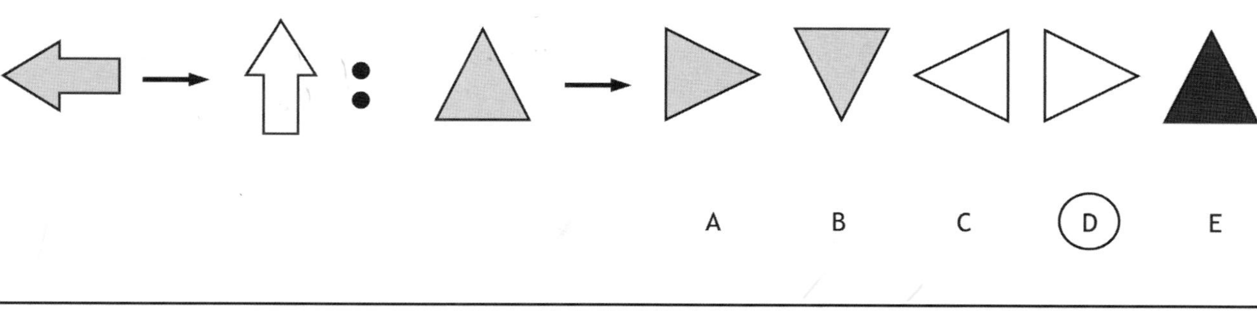

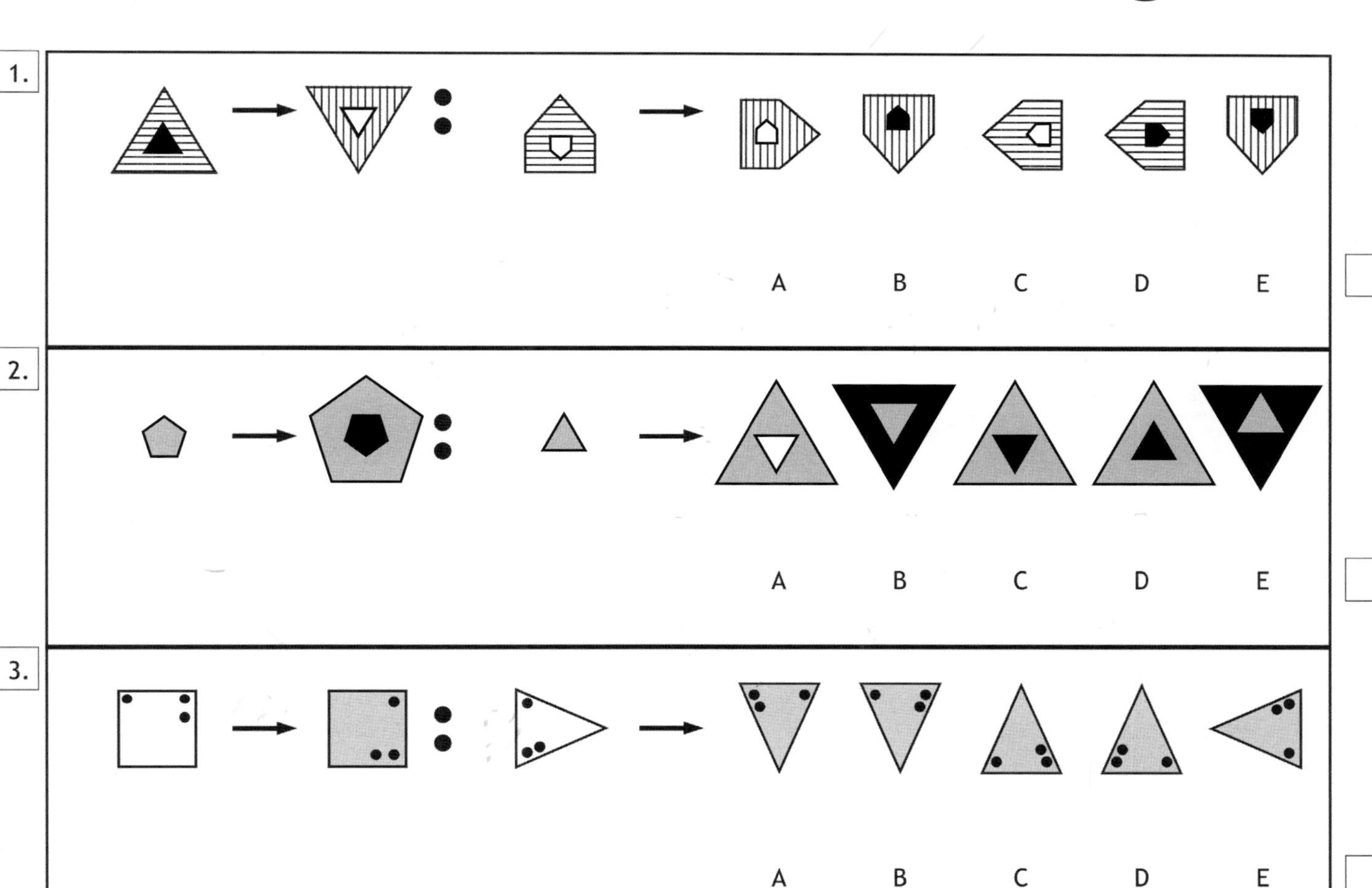

Page 4.2

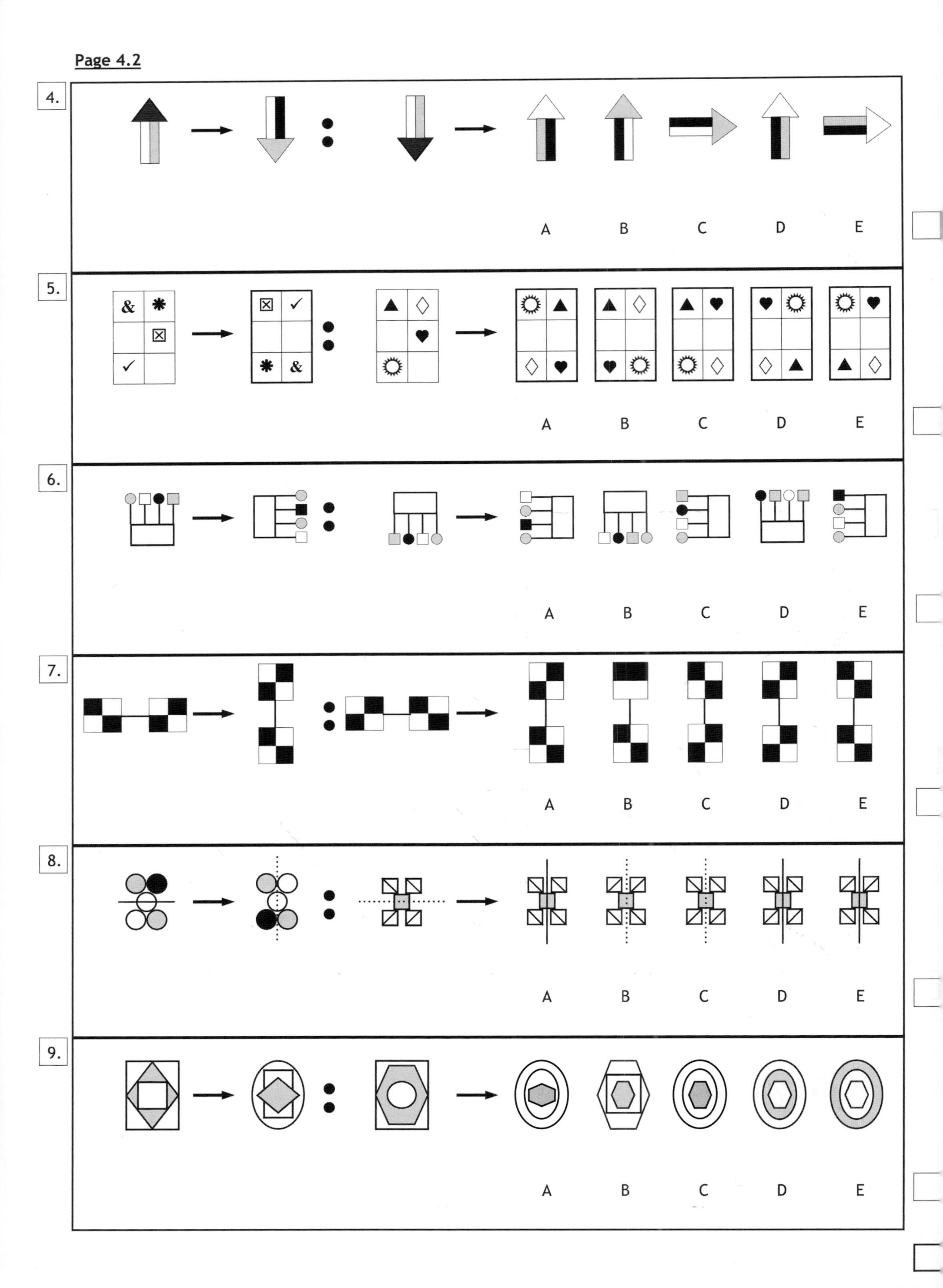

Section B

There are figures drawn in three sections of the large square on the left hand side of the page. One of the small squares is empty. This square can be filled by only one of the five boxes on the right.

Choose the box that you think will best complete the large square and circle the letter on the answer sheet, or mark the appropriate box on the multiple choice answer sheet.

Example:

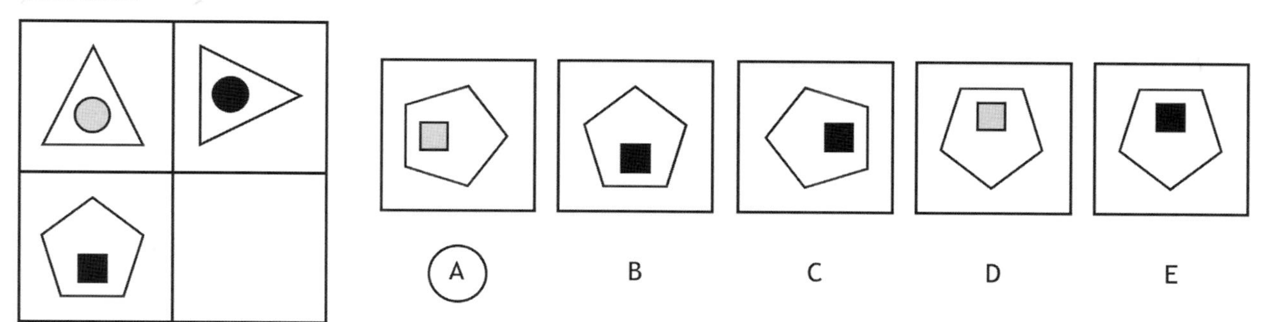

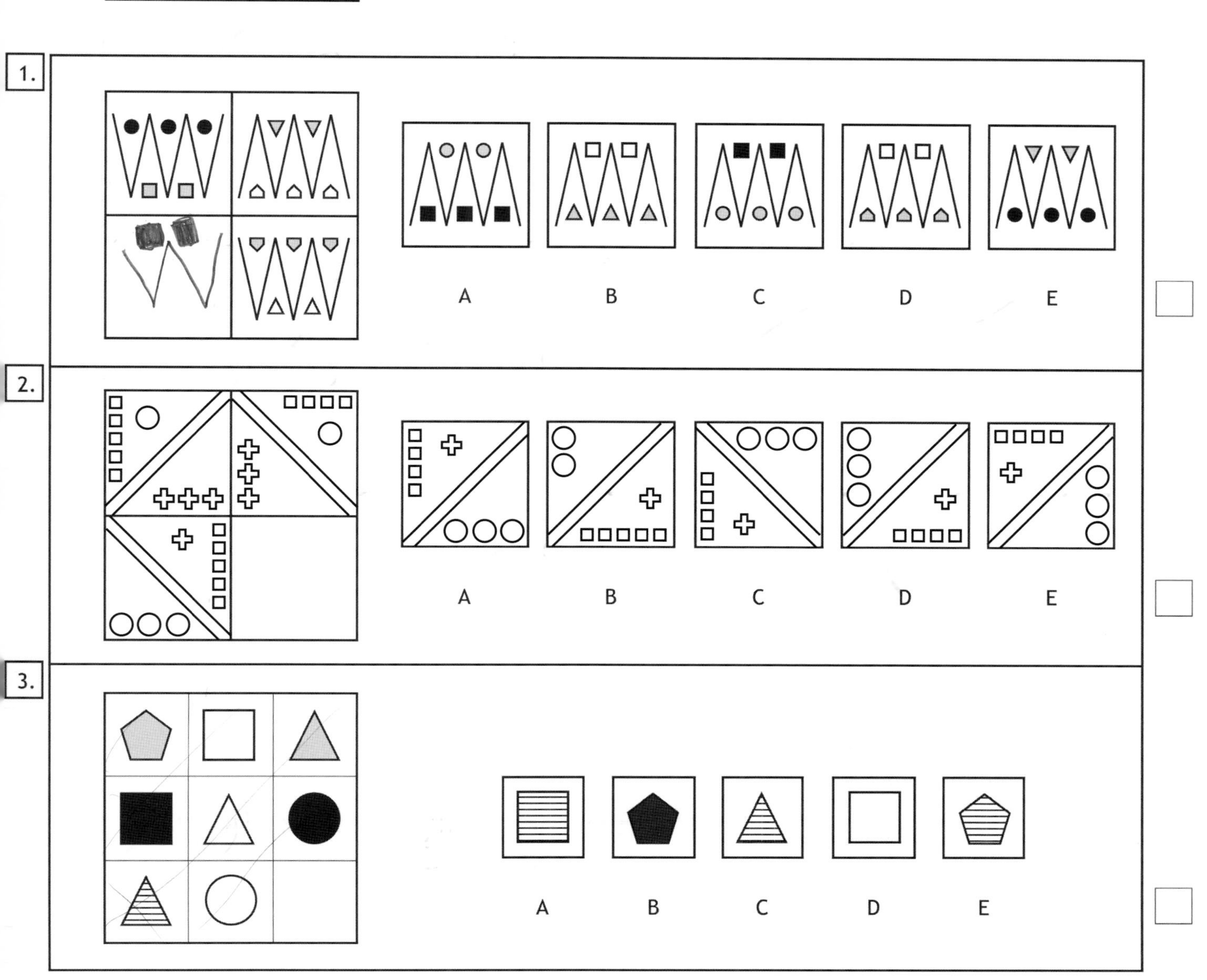

Page 4.4

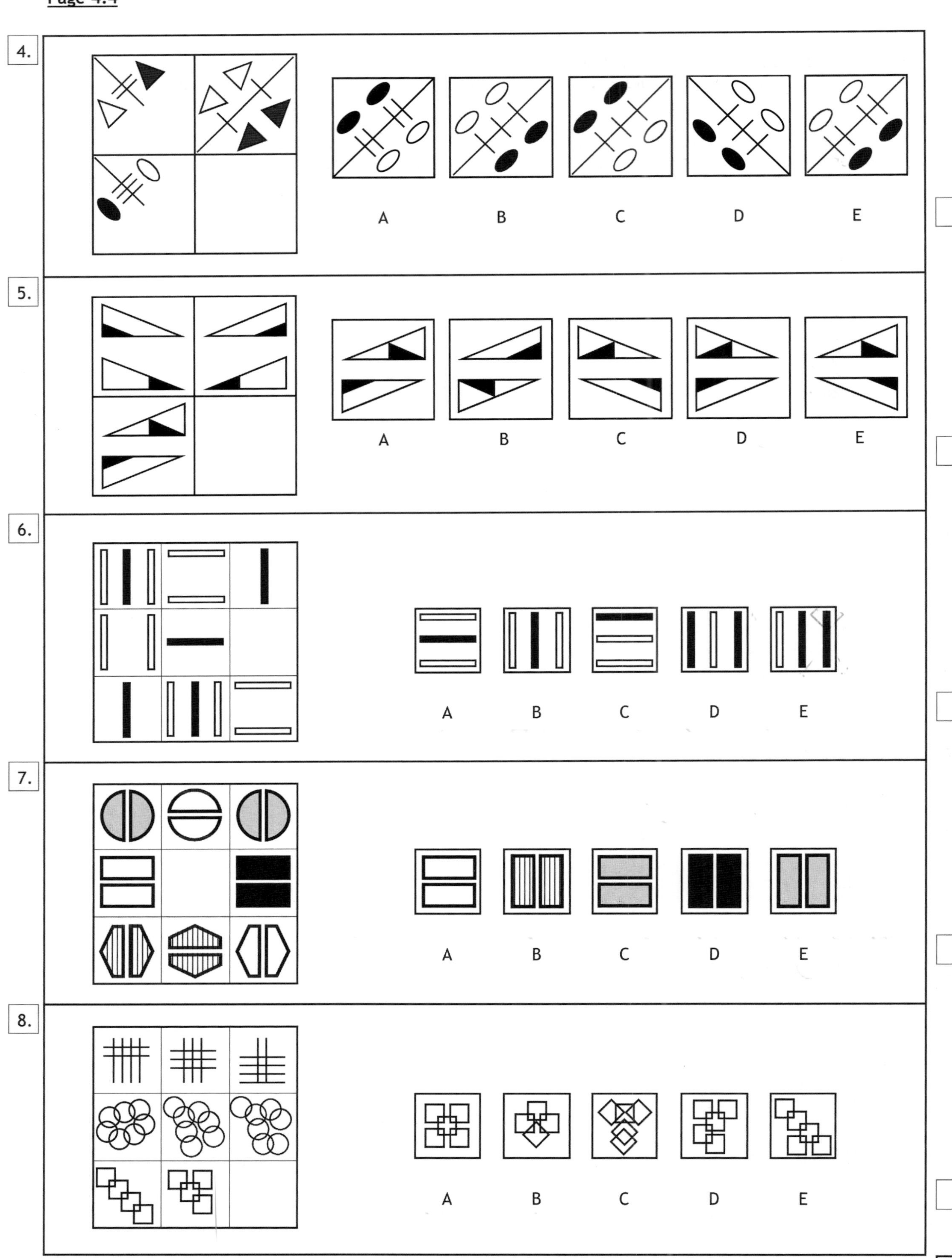

Section C

The shapes drawn on the left hand side of the page have been given letter codes that describe certain aspects of their appearance. Using this information you can find the code for the single shape.

Choose the code that you think describes the single shape and circle the letter on the answer sheet, or mark the appropriate box on the multiple choice answer sheet.

Example:

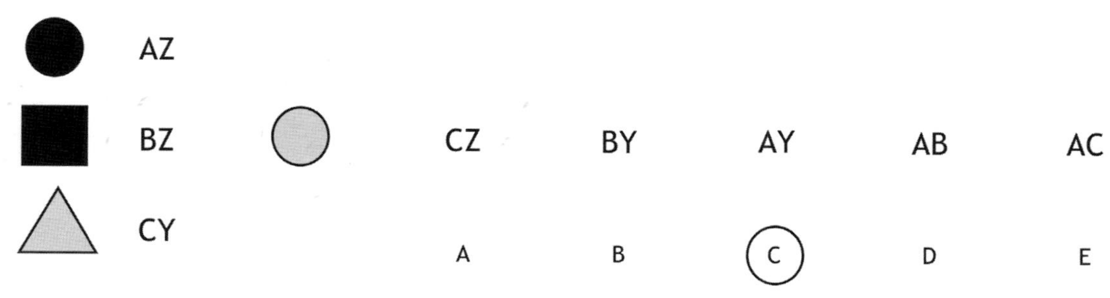

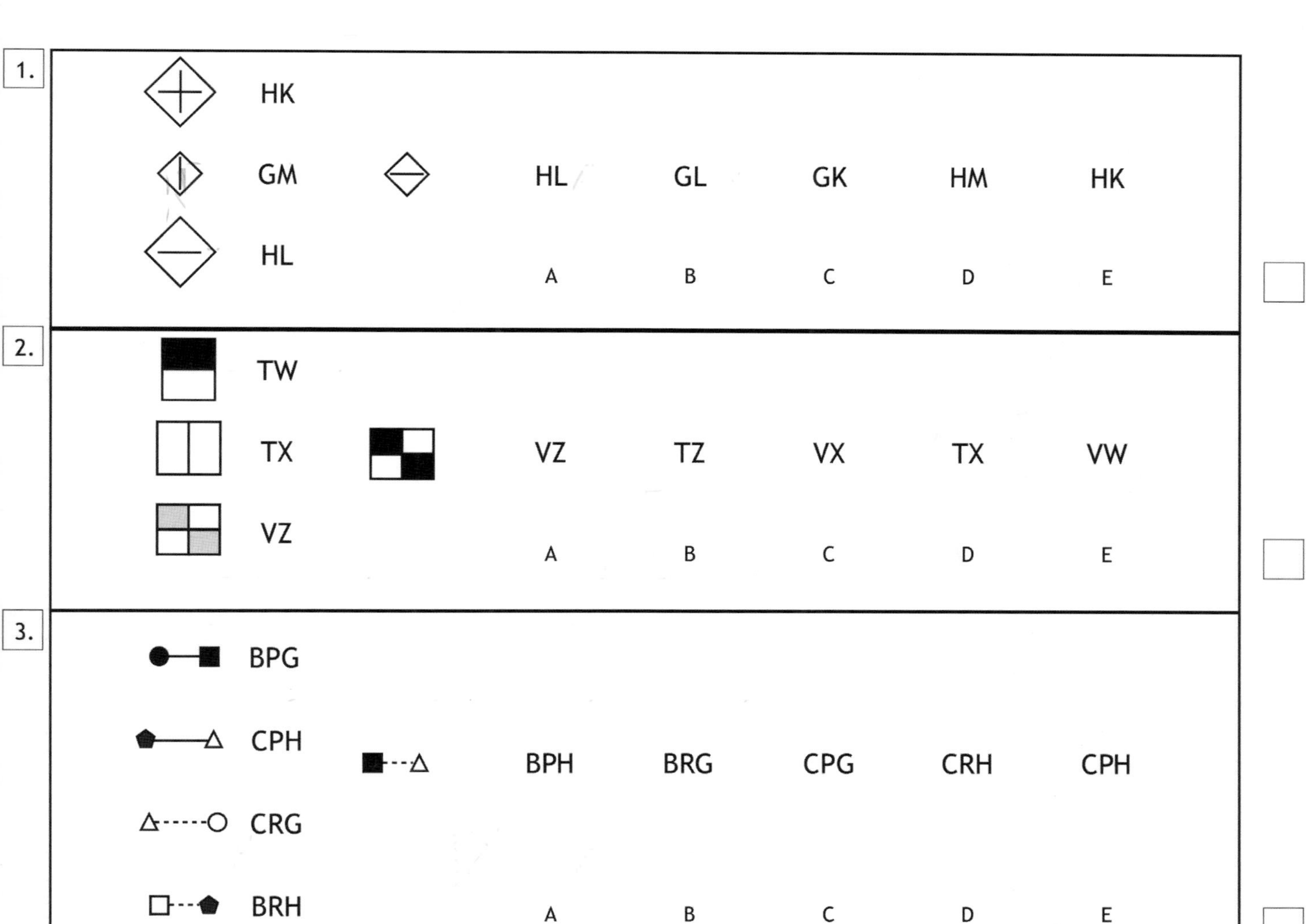

Page 4.6

4.

PAY							
QAX		QBY	QAY	PAX	PBY	PAZ
PBZ		A	B	C	D	E

5.

XMB						
ZNB		YNB	ZNB	ZMC	YNC	XNC
YMC		A	B	C	D	E

6.

DPF						
ARE		DPH	DRE	ARF	CPH	BPE
CPF						
BRH		A	B	C	D	E

7.

GRX						
HSY		GSX	HRT	GTX	GRX	HTY
GTY						
HRX		A	B	C	D	E

8.

MA						
MC		MA	KD	MC	KA	KC
KD						
KA		A	B	C	D	E

Section D

On the left hand side of the page there are two shapes that are similar. On the right hand side there are five other shapes.

You must choose one shape of the five that you is most alike to the first two and circle its letter on the answer sheet, or mark the appropriate box on the multiple choice answer sheet.

Example:

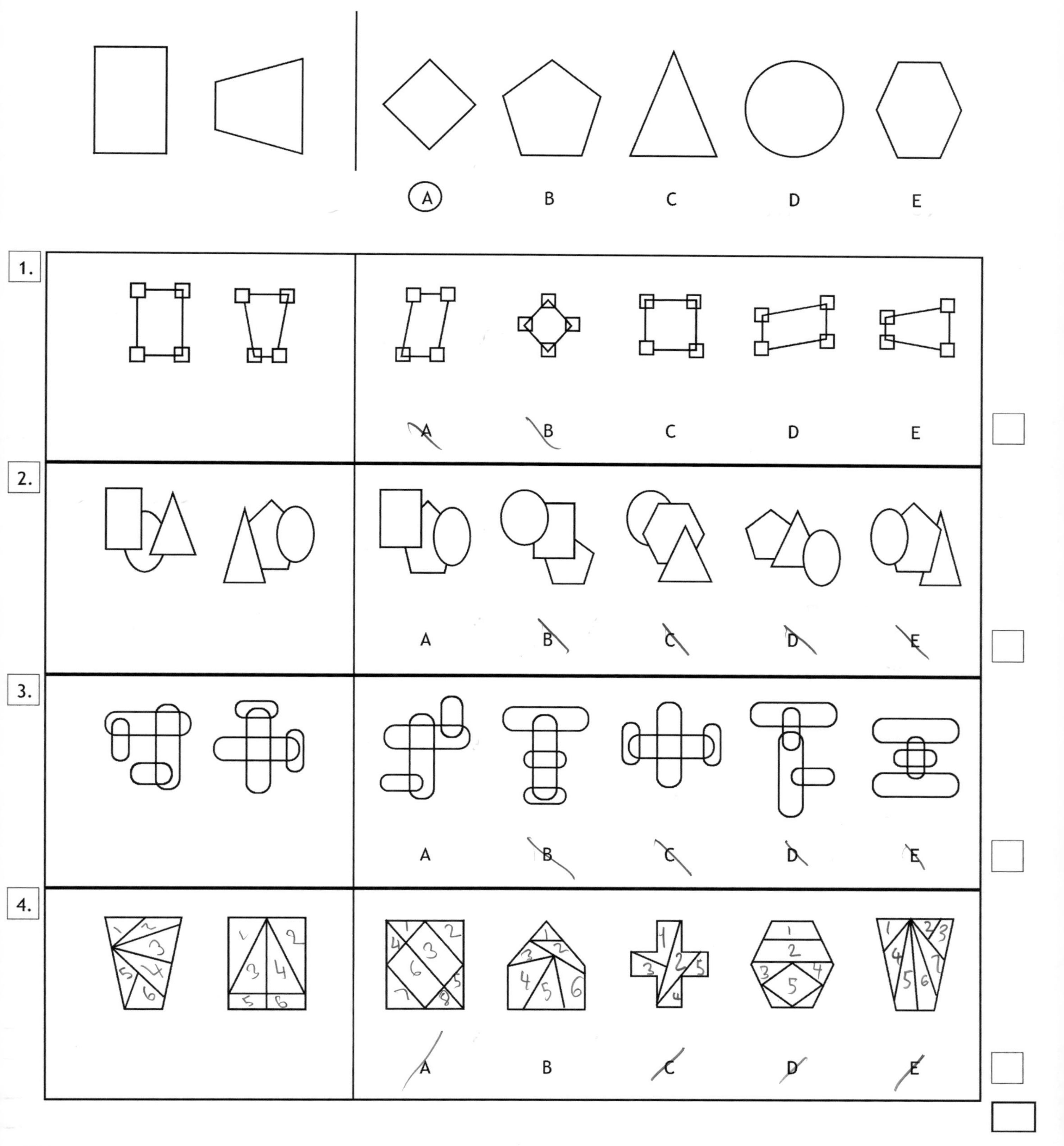

Page 4.8

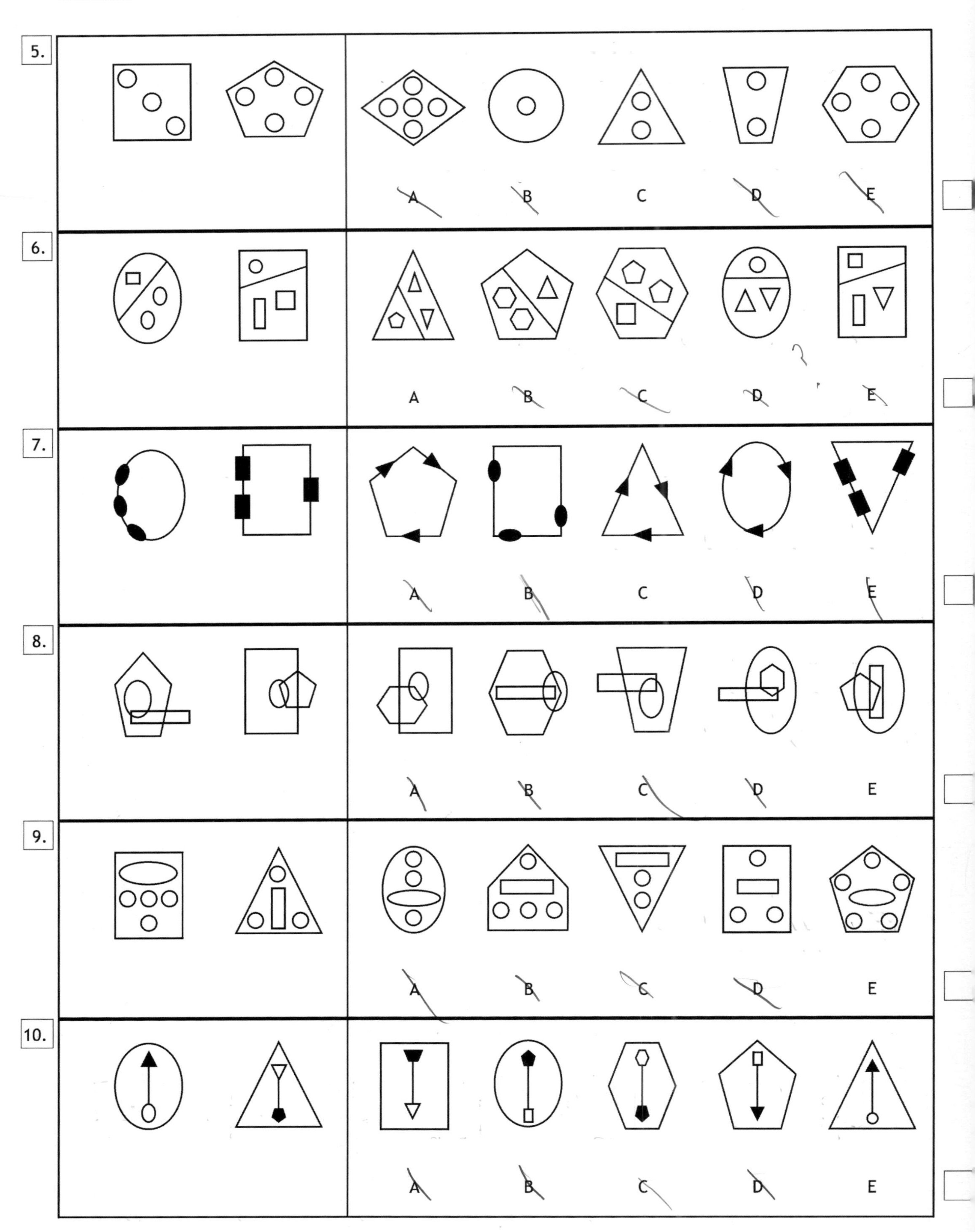

Practice Paper 5.

There are 35 questions in four sections on this paper. You have 30 minutes to complete this test.

Circle your answers carefully on the answer sheet or place a mark in the multiple choice answer box on the separate sheet.

Section A

On the left of the page is a sequence figures in five boxes. One of the boxes is empty. This box can be filled by the figure in one of the five boxes on the right.

Choose the box you think will best complete the sequence and circle the letter on the ans wer sheet, or mark the appropriate box on the multiple choice answer sheet.

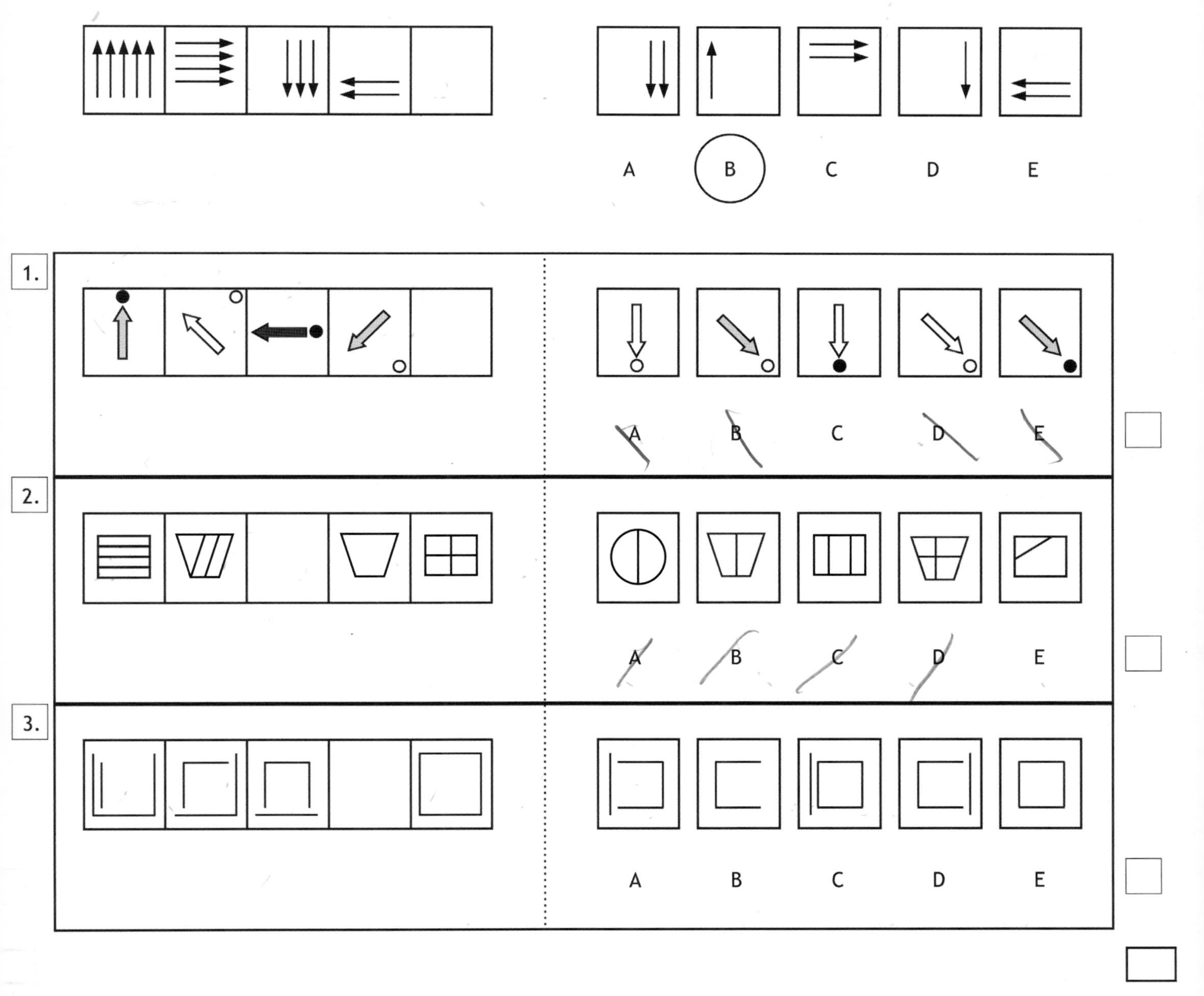

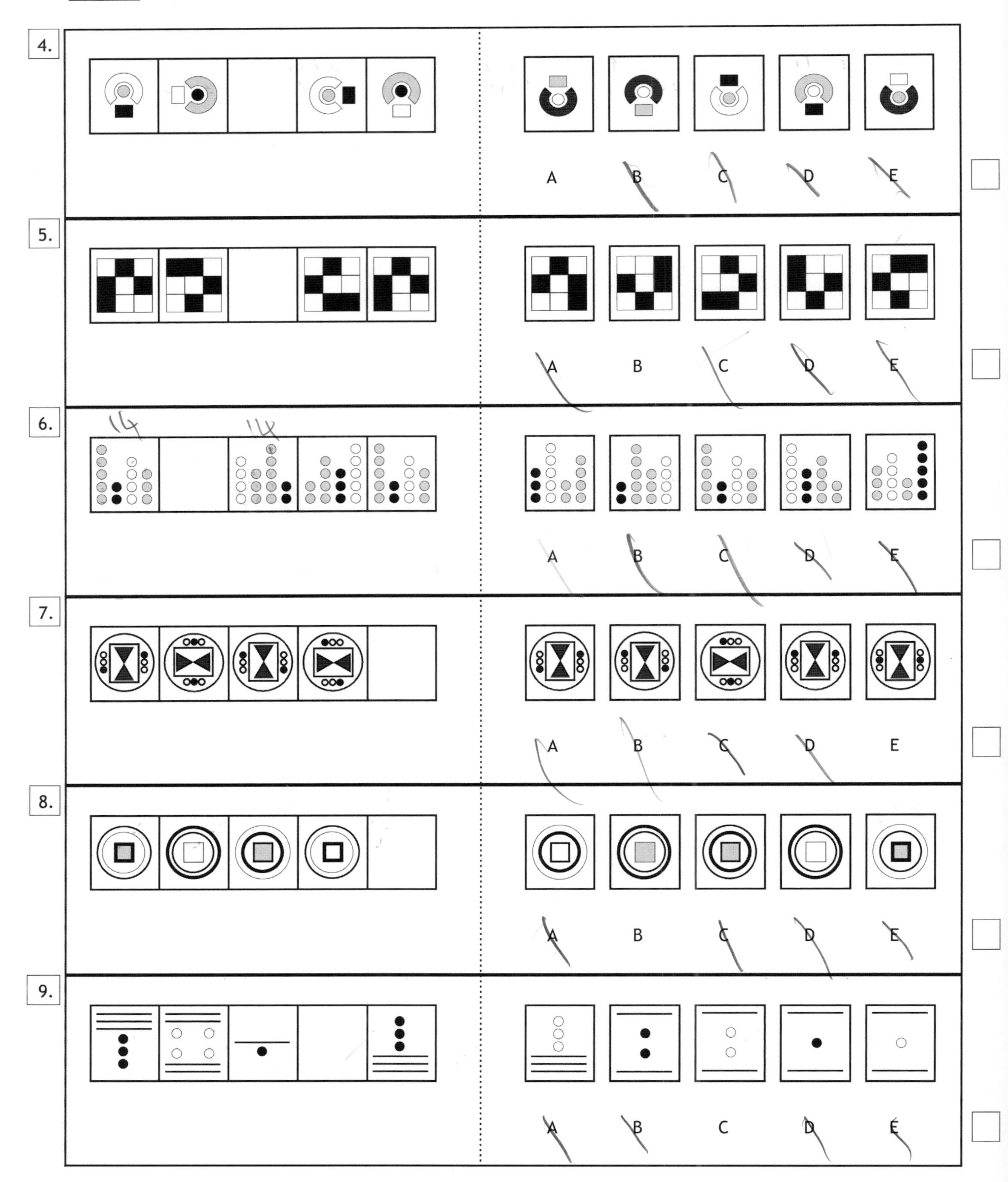
4.
A
B
C
D
E
5.
A
B
C
D
E
6.
A
B
C
D
E
7.
A
B
C
D
E
8.
A
B
C
D
E
9.
A
B
C
D
E

Section B

On the left of each question are two figures connected by an arrow. You must work out how the second figure is related to the first. Now look at the third figure. Which of the five other figures that follow is related to the third in the same way that the second is to the first?

Choose the shape that you think goes with the third shape and circle the letter on the answer sheet, or mark the appropriate box on the multiple choice answer sheet.

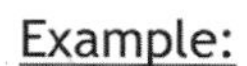

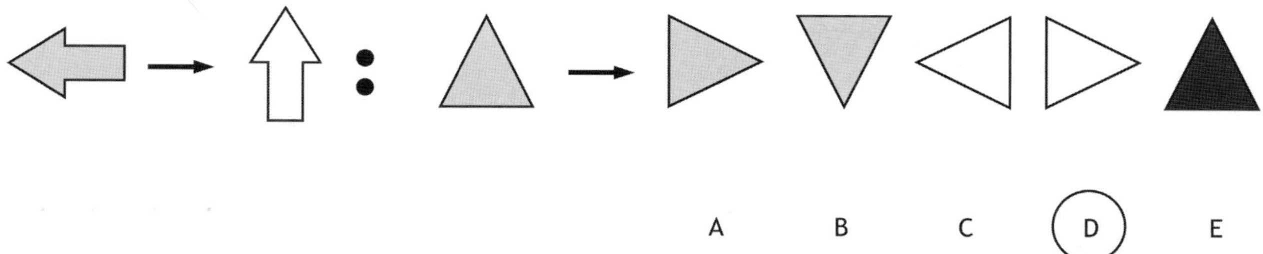

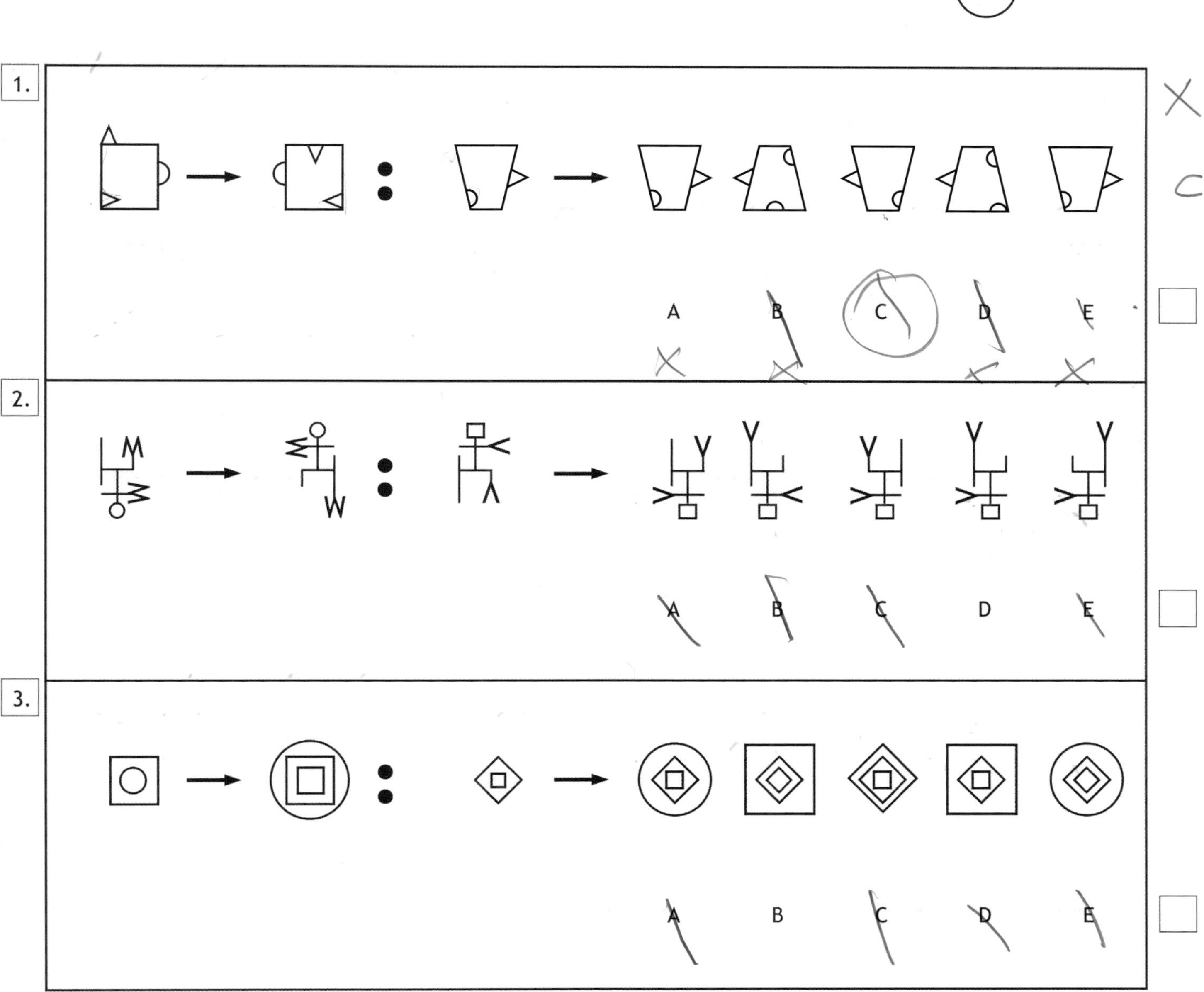

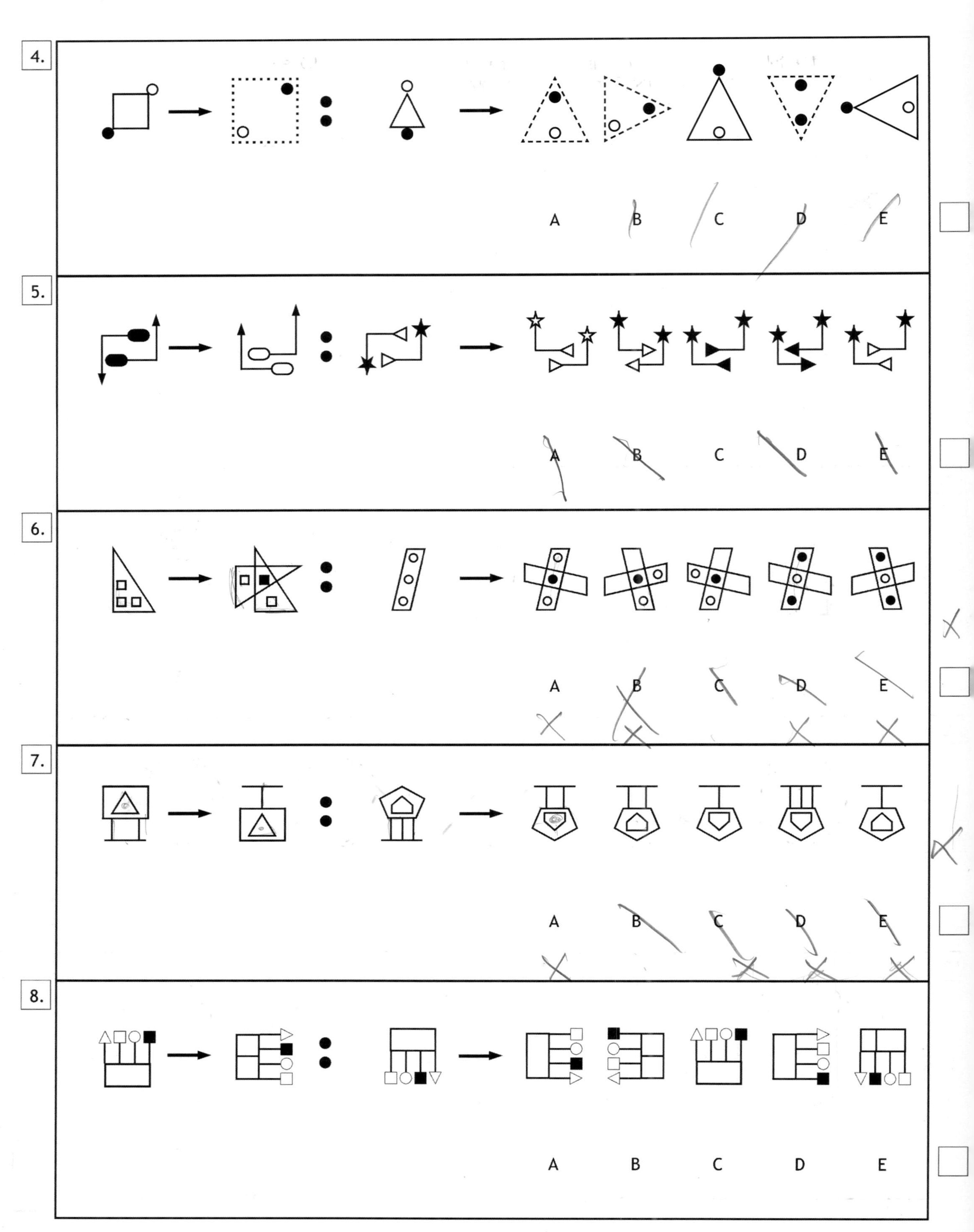
4.
A
B
C
D
E
5.
A
B
C
D
E
6.
A
B
C
D
E
7.
A
B
C
D
E
8.
A
B
C
D
E

Section C

Each of the following questions consists of five shapes in a row. They all have something in common, except one. You must find the odd one out.

Choose the shape that you think does not go with the other four and circle the letter on the answer sheet, or mark the appropriate box on the multiple choice answer sheet.

Example:

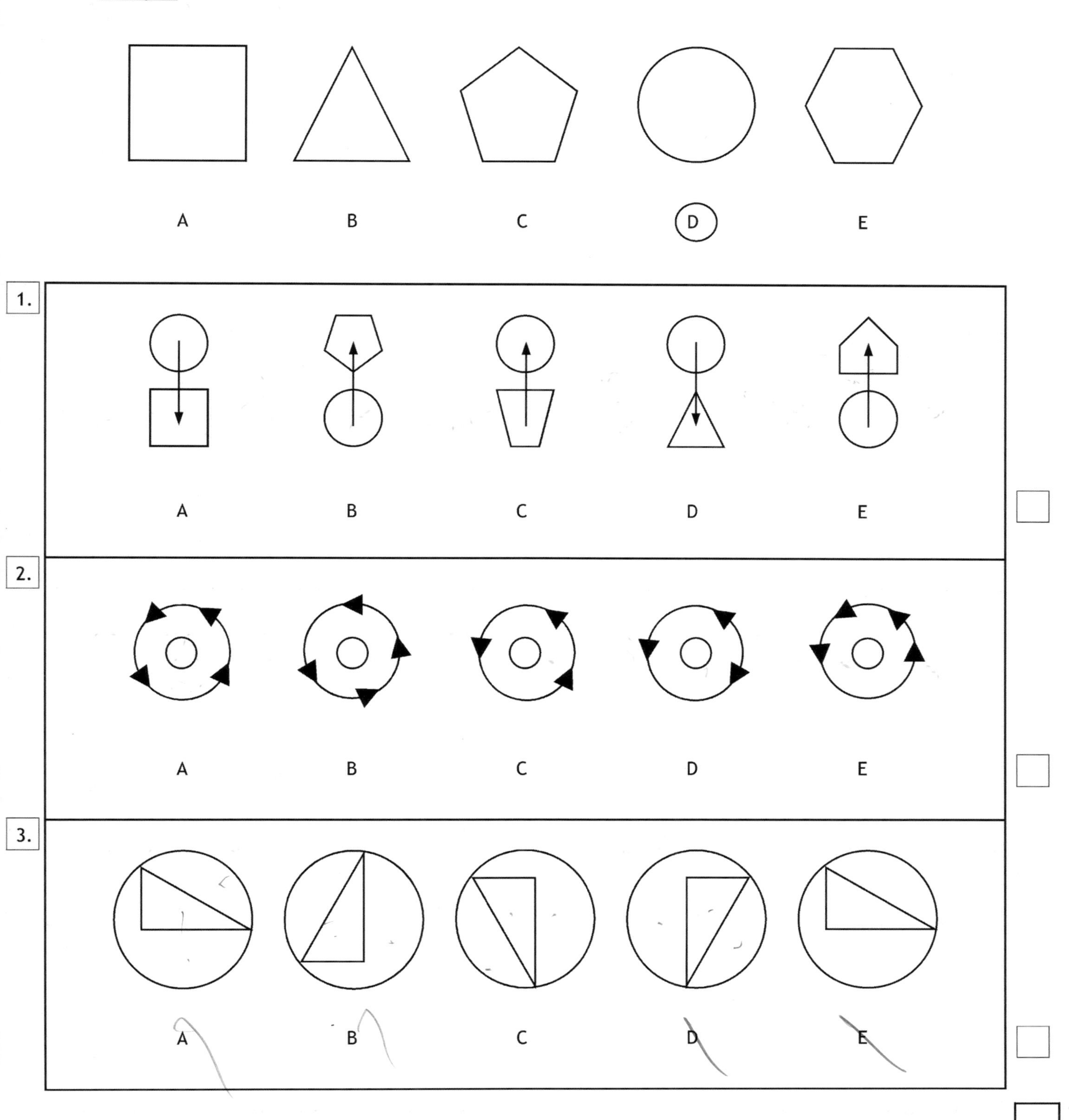

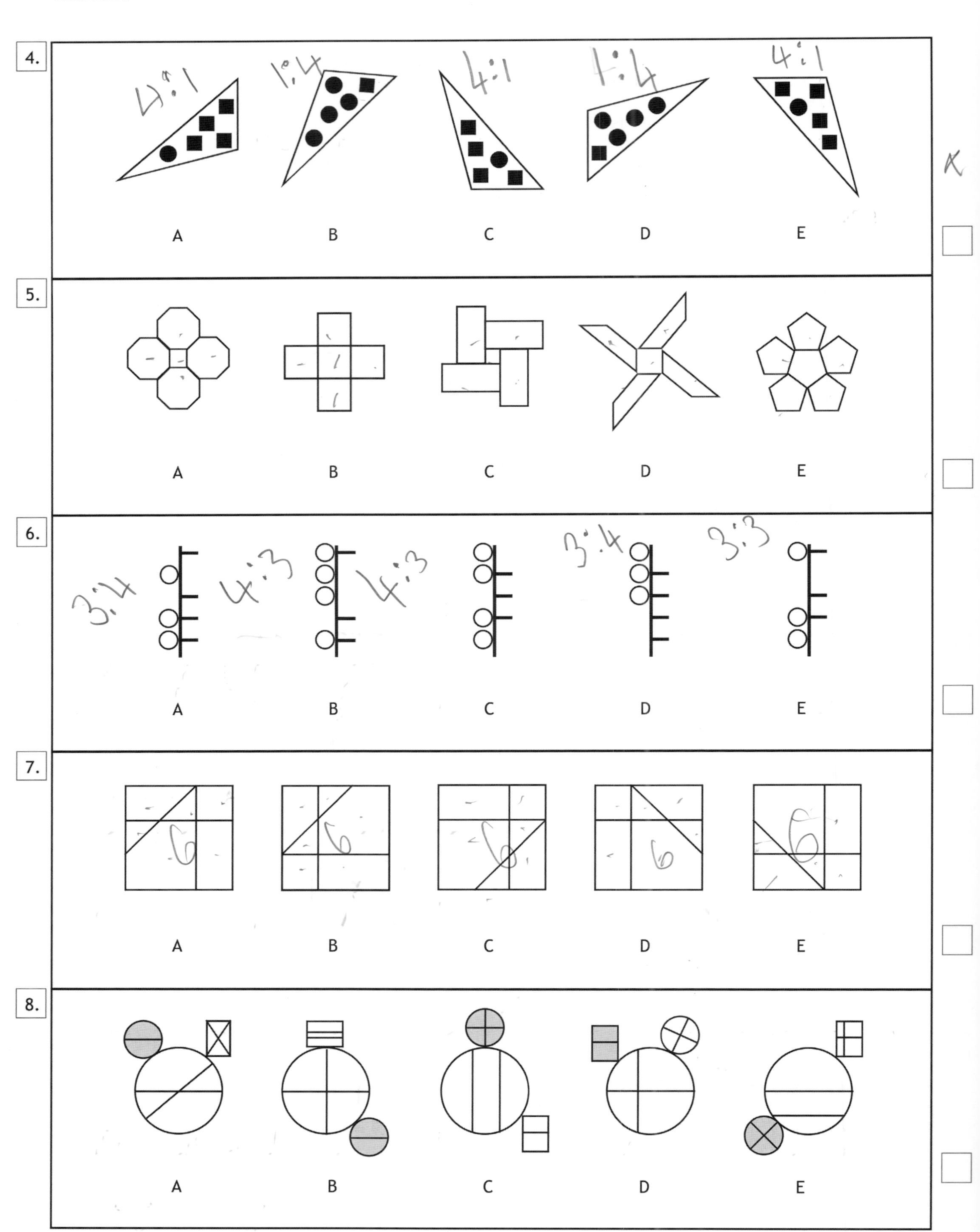
4.
A
B
C
D
E
5.
A
B
C
D
E
6.
A
B
C
D
E
7.
A
B
C
D
E
8.
A
B
C
D
E

Section D

The shapes drawn in the boxes on the left hand side of the page have been given letter codes that describe certain aspects of their appearance. Using this information you can find the code for the shape in the box on the right.

Choose the code letters that you think describes the shape in the box on the right hand side and circle the letter on the answer sheet, or mark the appropriate box on the multiple choice answer sheet.

Example:

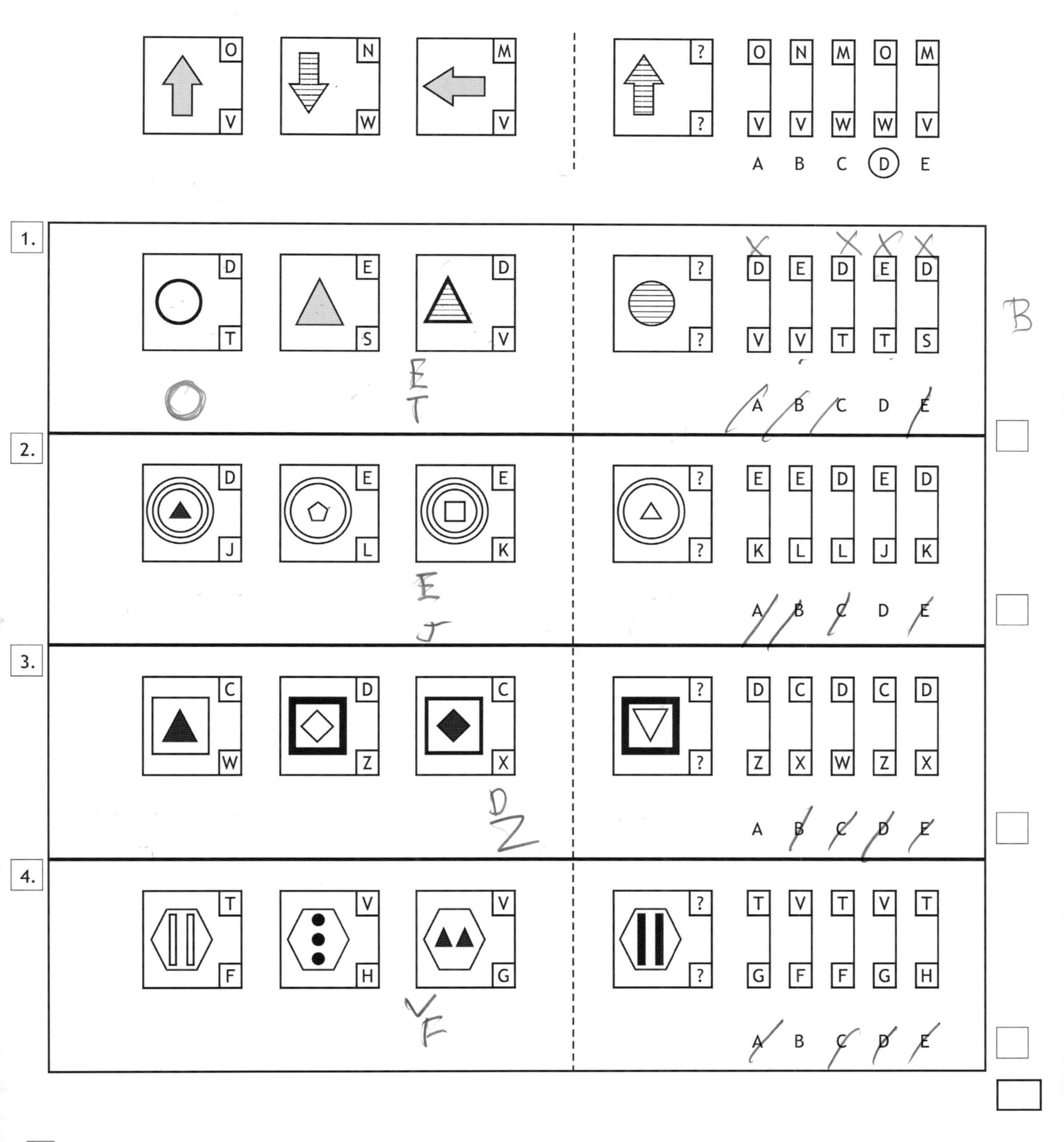

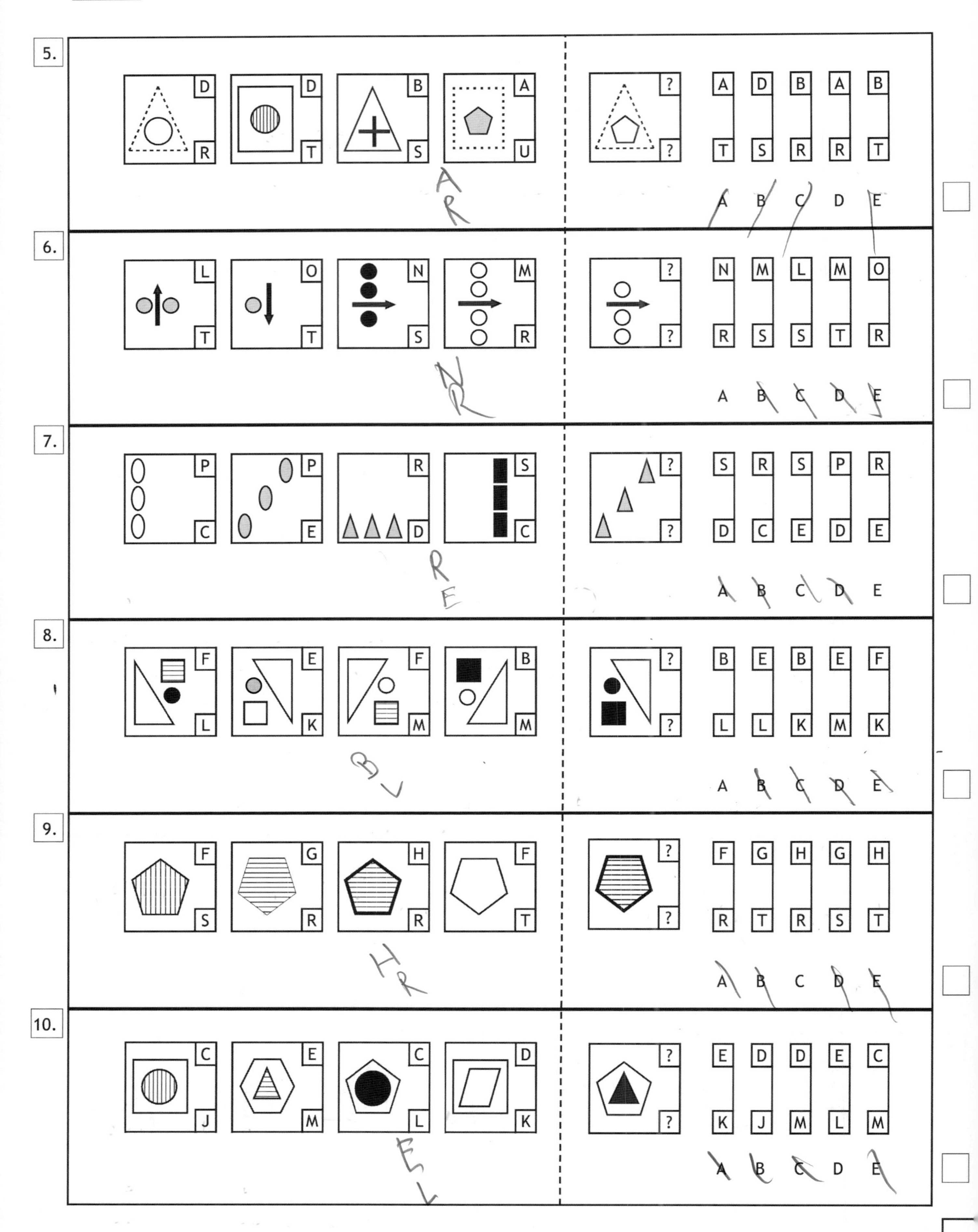

Practice Paper 6.

There are 35 questions in four sections on this paper. You have 30 minutes to complete this test.

Circle your answers carefully on the answer sheet or place a mark in the multiple choice answer box on the separate sheet.

Section A

On the left hand side of the page there are two shapes that are similar. On the right hand side there are five other shapes.

You must choose one shape of the five that is most like the first two and circle its letter on the answer sheet, or mark the appropriate box on the multiple choice answer sheet.

Example:

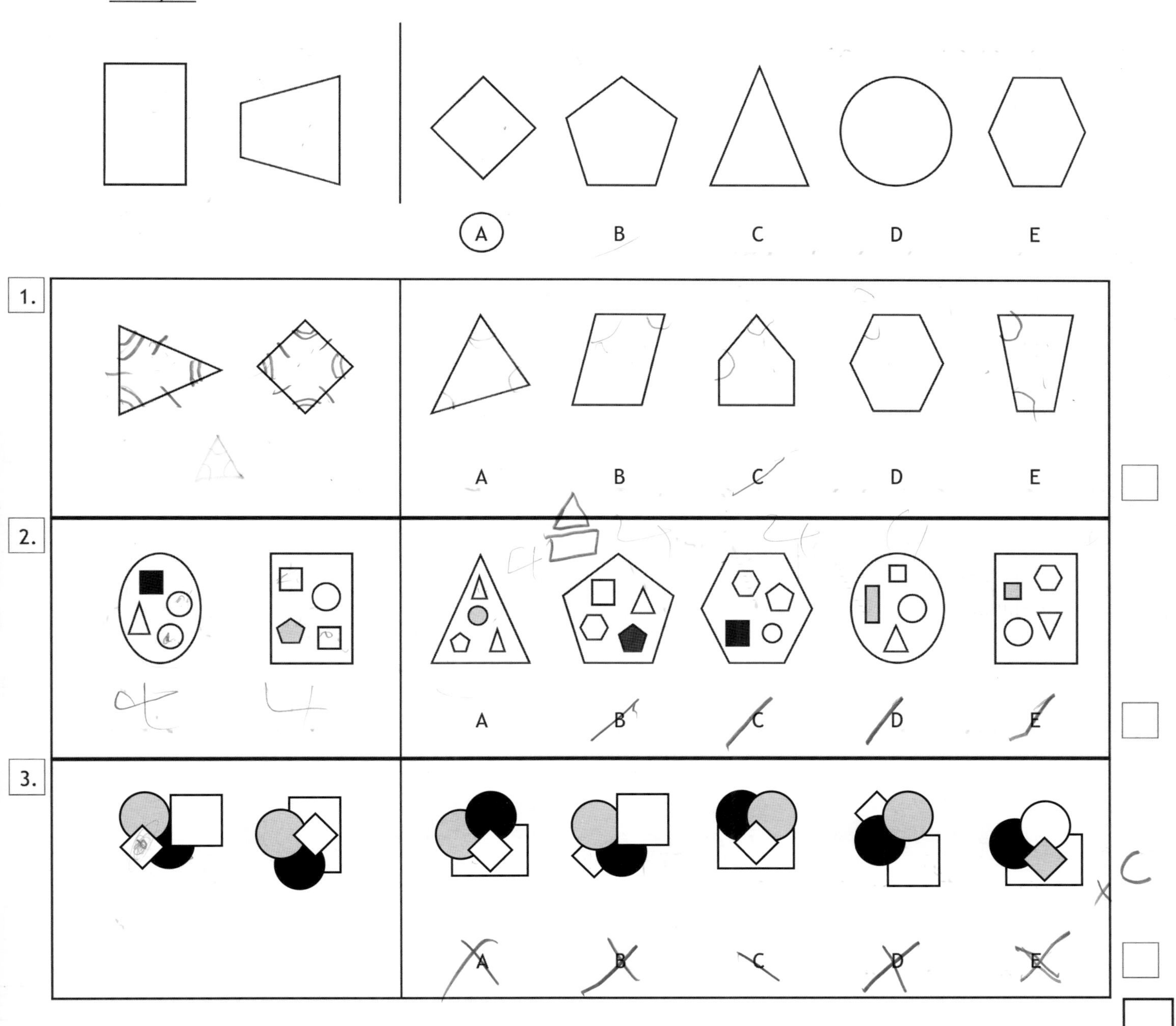

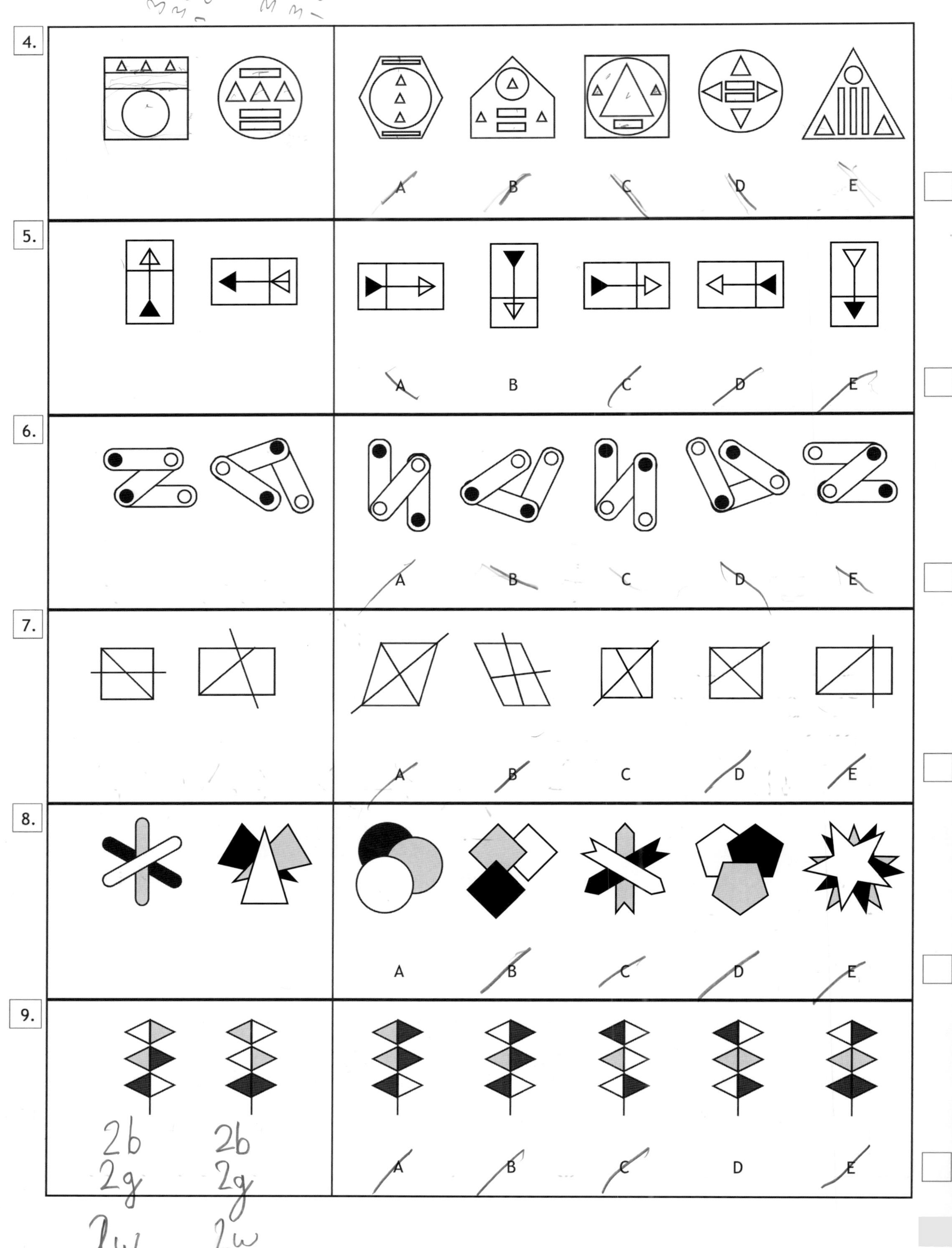
4.
A
B
C
D
E
5.
A
B
C
D
E
6.
A
B
C
D
E
7.
A
B
C
D
E
8.
A
B
C
D
E
9.
A
B
C
D
E

Section B

There are figures drawn in three sections of the large square on the left hand side of the page. One of the small squares is empty. This square can be filled by only one of the five boxes on the right.

Choose the box that you think will best complete the large square and circle the letter on the answer sheet, or mark the appropriate box on the multiple choice answer sheet.

Example:

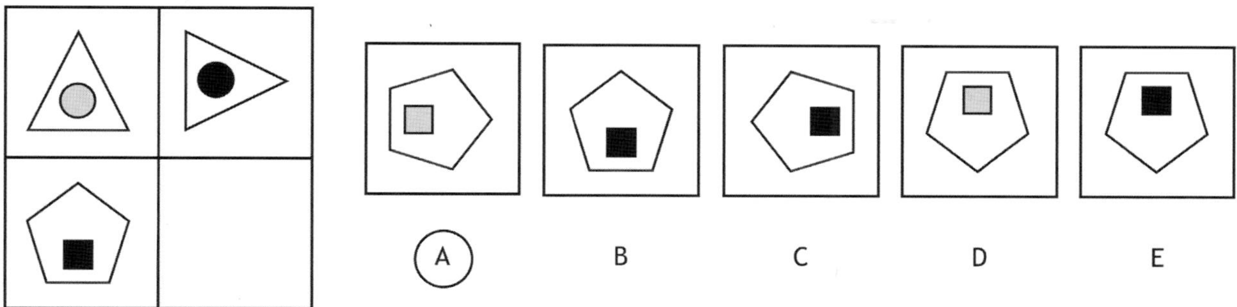

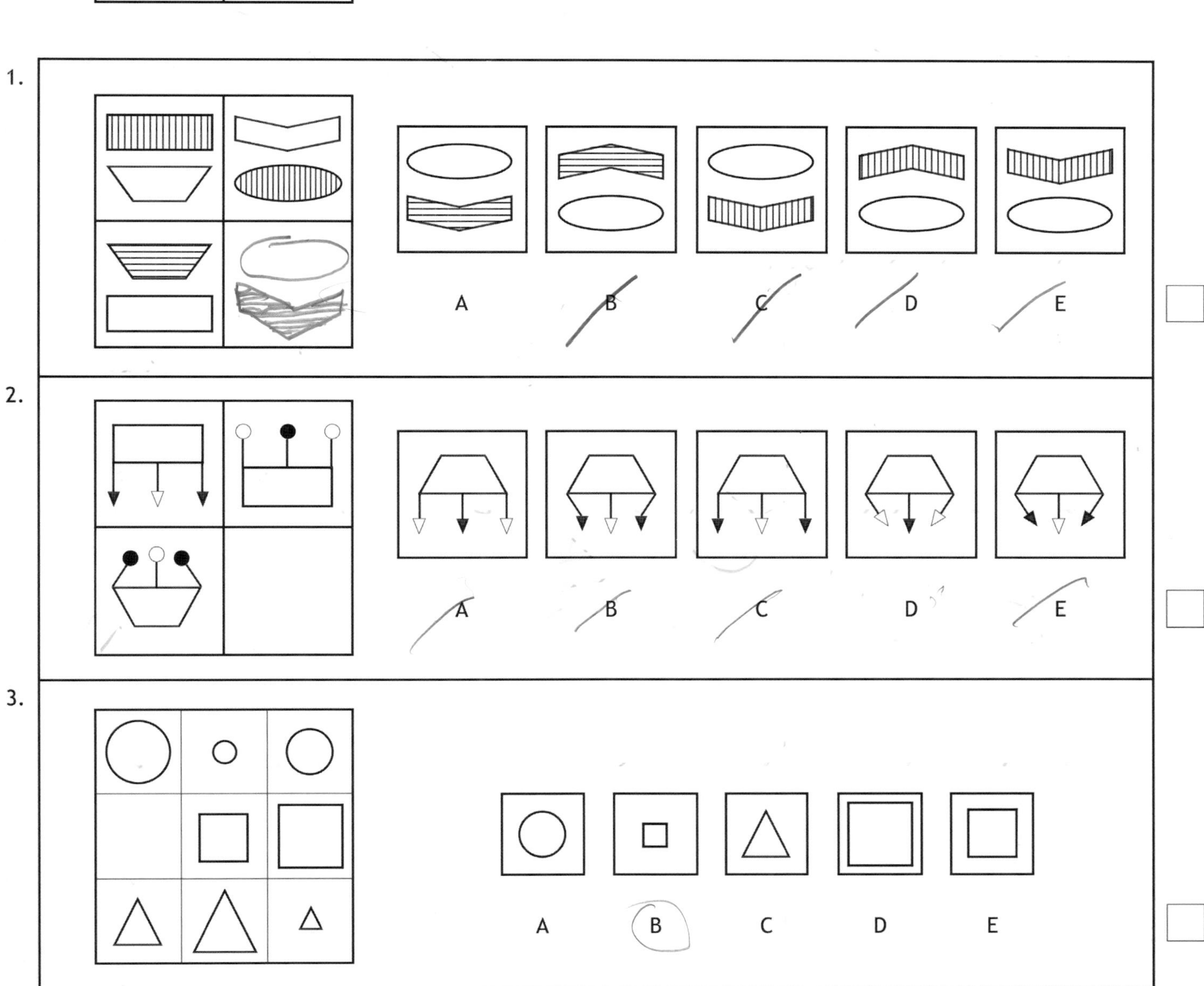

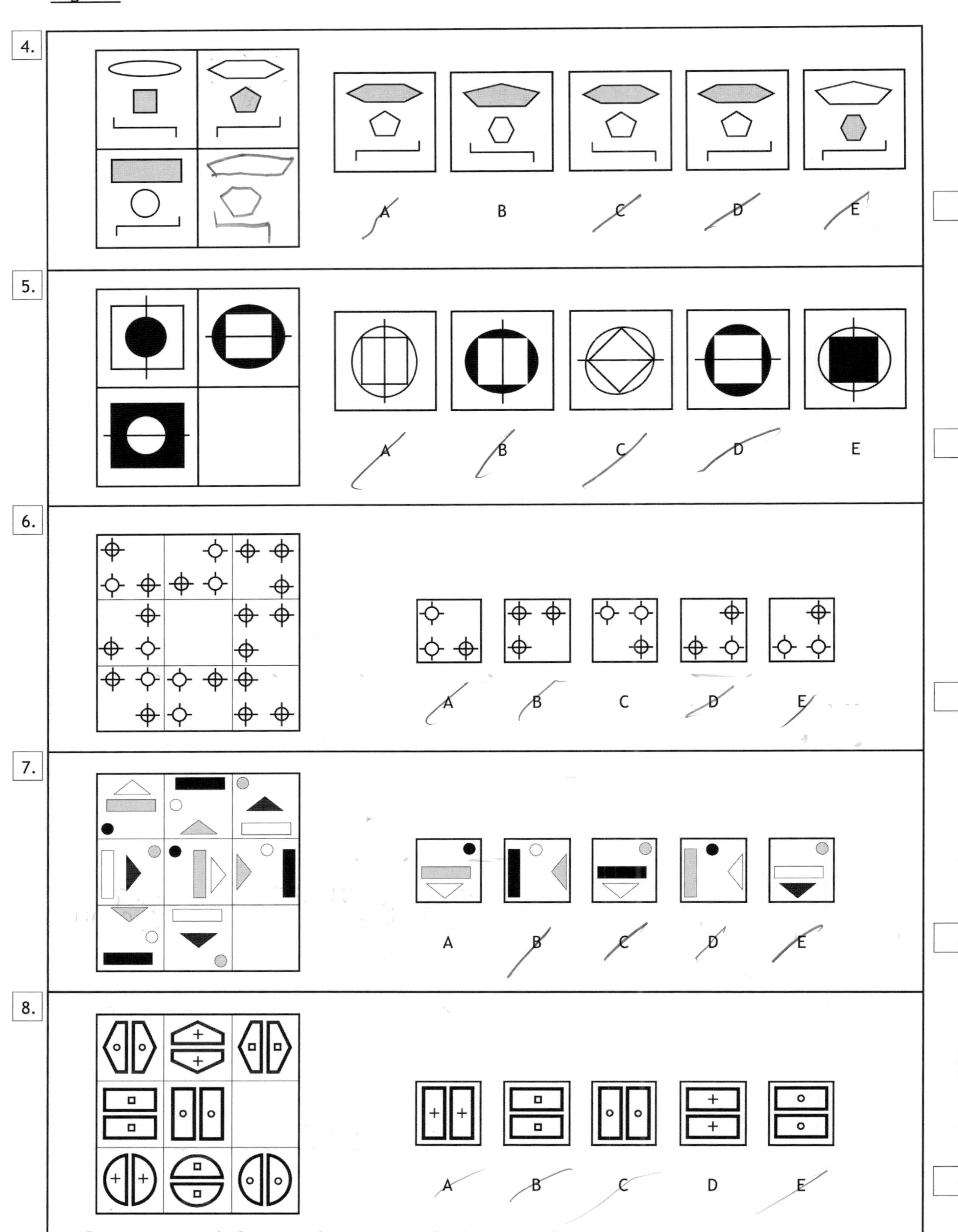
4.
A
B
C
D
E
5.
A
B
C
D
E
6.
A
B
C
D
E
7.
A
B
C
D
E
8.
A
B
C
D
E

Section C

On the left of the page is a sequence of figures in five boxes. One of the boxes is empty. This box can be filled by only one of the figures in the five boxes on the right.

Choose the figure that you think will best complete the sequence and circle the letter on the answer sheet, or mark the appropriate box on the multiple choice answer sheet.

Example:

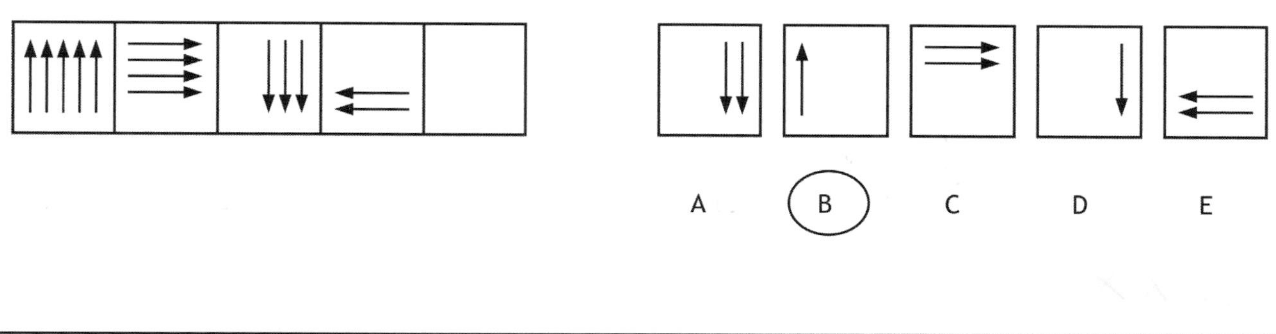

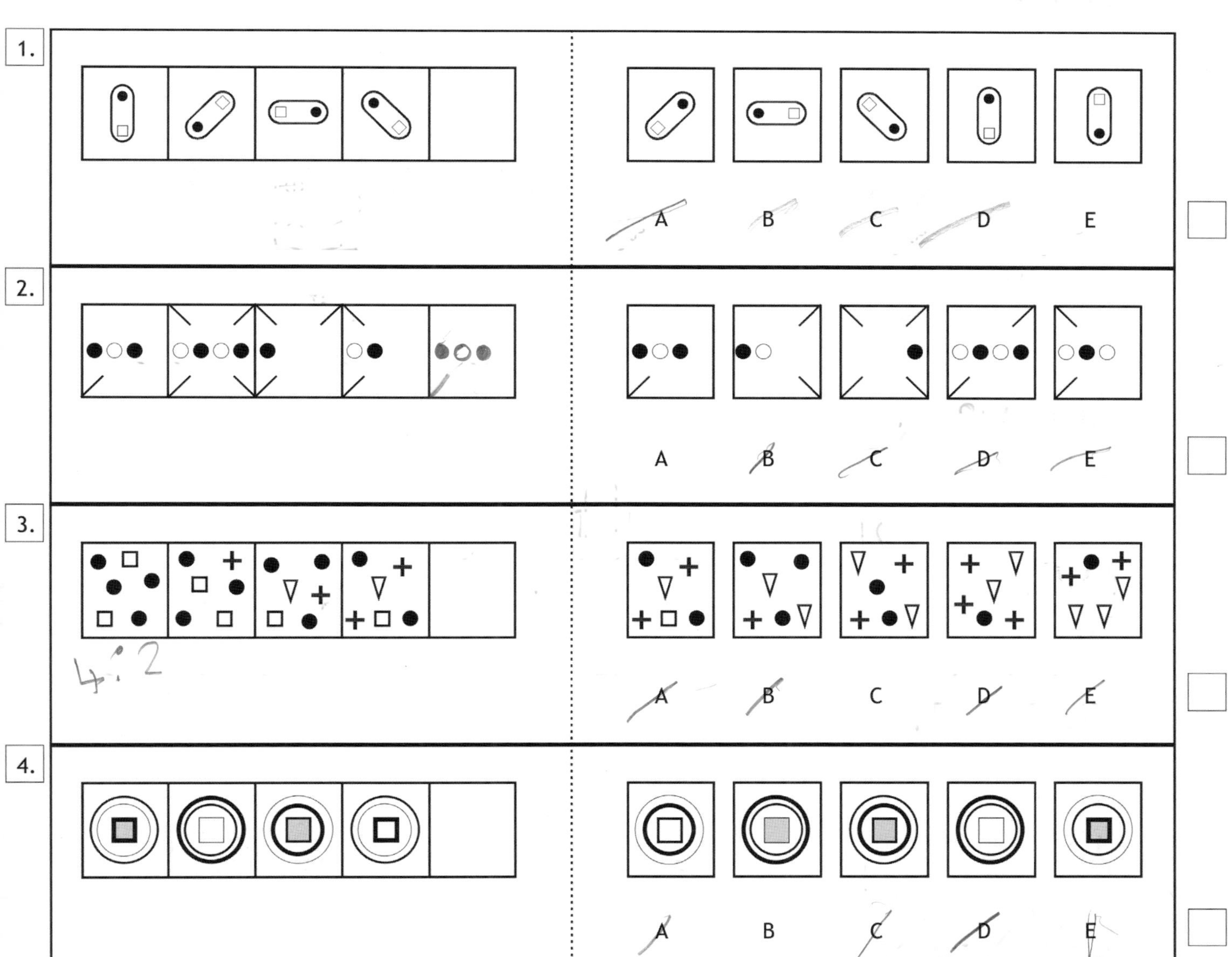

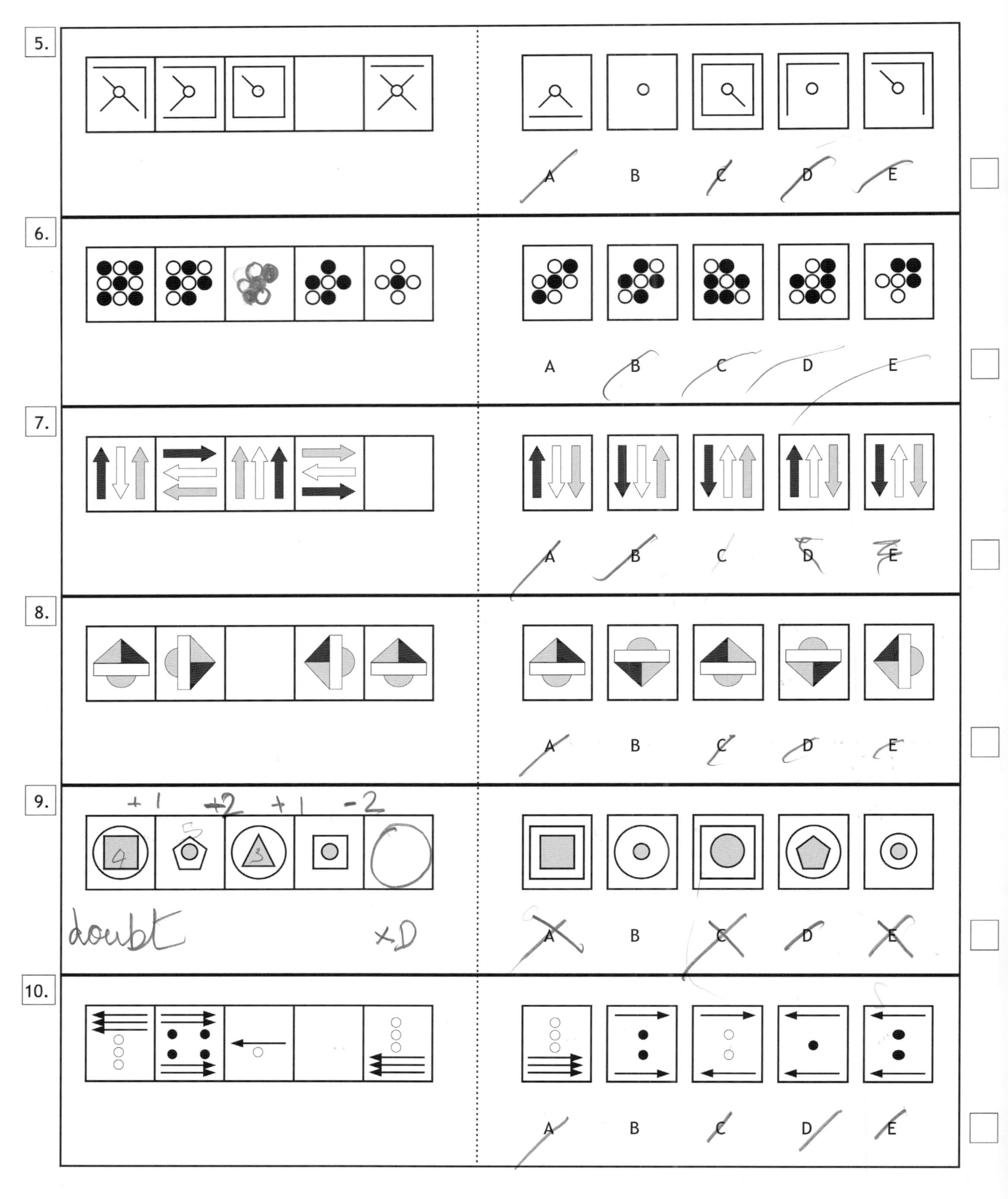
5.
A
B
C
D
E
6.
A
B
C
D
E
7.
A
B
C
D
E
8.
A
B
C
D
E
9.
+1
+2
+1
-2
doubt
x D
A
B
C
D
E
10.
A
B
C
D
E

Section D

The shapes drawn on the left hand side of the page have been given letter codes that describe certain aspects of their appearance. Using this information you can find the code for the single shape.

Choose the code that you think describes the single shape and circle the letter on the answer sheet, or mark the appropriate box on the multiple choice answer sheet.

Example:

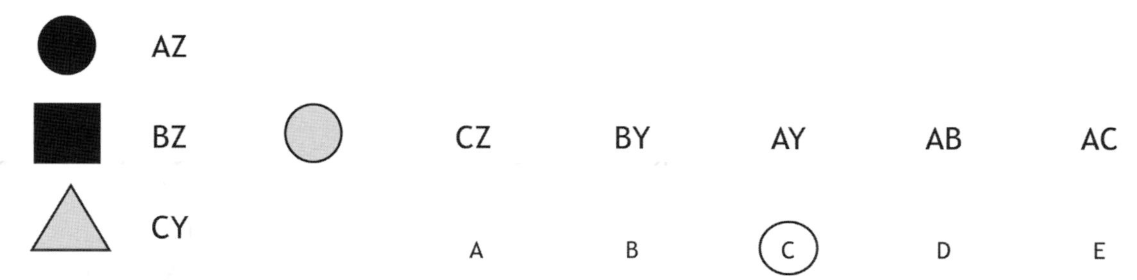

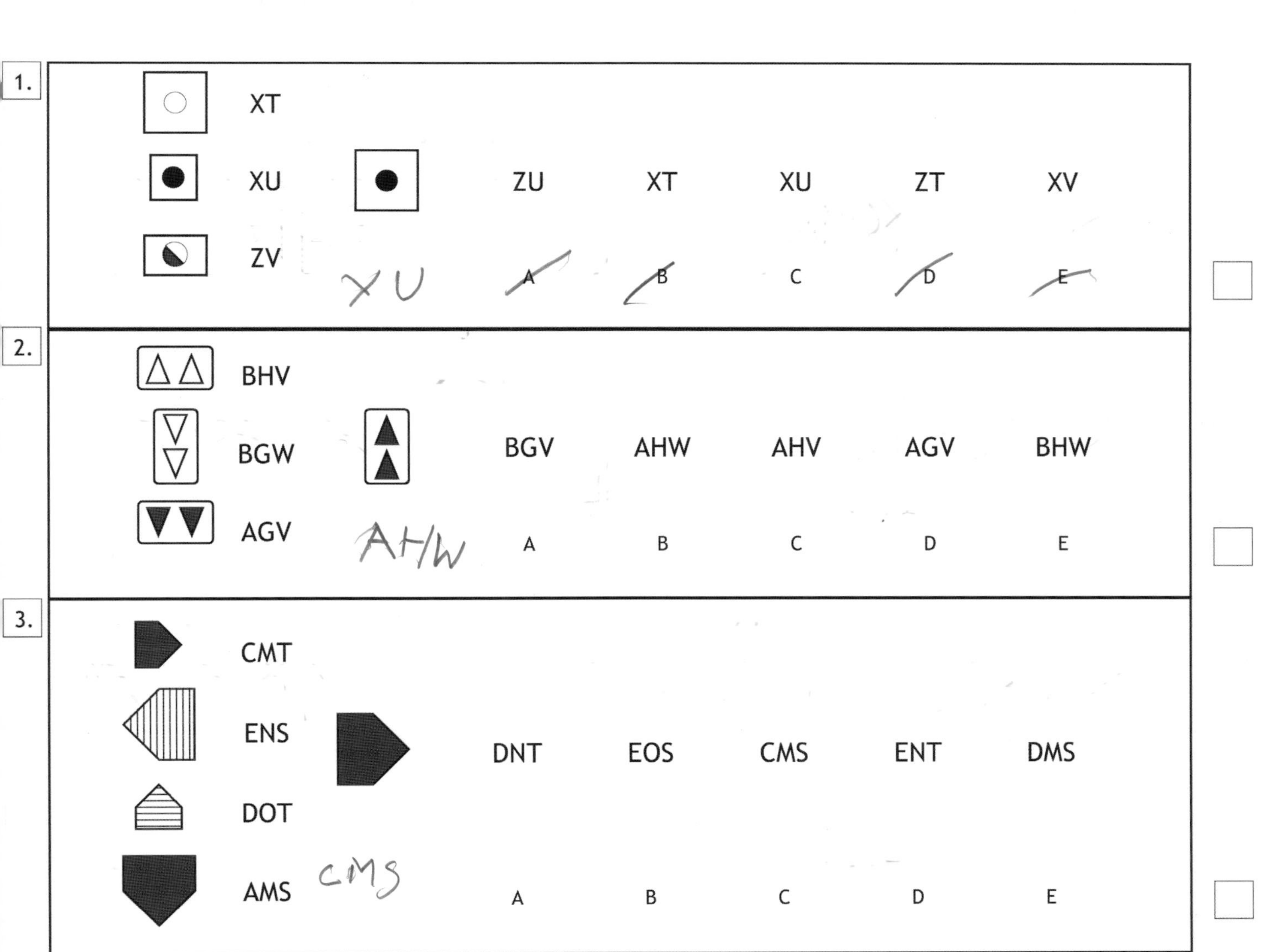

Page 6.8

4.

AZT						
BZS		AYS	BYS	CYS	AZS	AZT
CYT	CYS	A	B	C	D	E

5.

PH						
QH		QH	PV	PH	RV	QV
RV	PV ✓	A	B	C	D	E

6.

XHT						
WFS		YGT	XGT	WHS	YGS	XFS
YHS						
WGT	XGT	A	B	C	D	E

7.

PDJ						
RCK		PDK	REJ	PDM	PEK	RCM
PEM	PEK					
RDL		A	B	C	D	E

8.

CWG						
BXH		AXG	CXH	DXJ	CWJ	BWJ
AWJ	BWJ					
DXG		A	B	C	D	E

Practice Paper 7.

There are 35 questions in four sections on this paper. You have 30 minutes to complete this test.

Circle your answers carefully on the answer sheet or place a mark in the multiple choice answer box on the separate sheet.

Section A

The shapes drawn in the boxes on the left hand side of the page have been given letter codes that describe certain aspects of their appearance. Using this information you can find the code for the shape in the box on the right.

Choose the code letters that you think describes the shape in the box on the right hand side and circle the letter on the answer sheet, or mark the appropriate box on the multiple choice answer sheet.

Example:

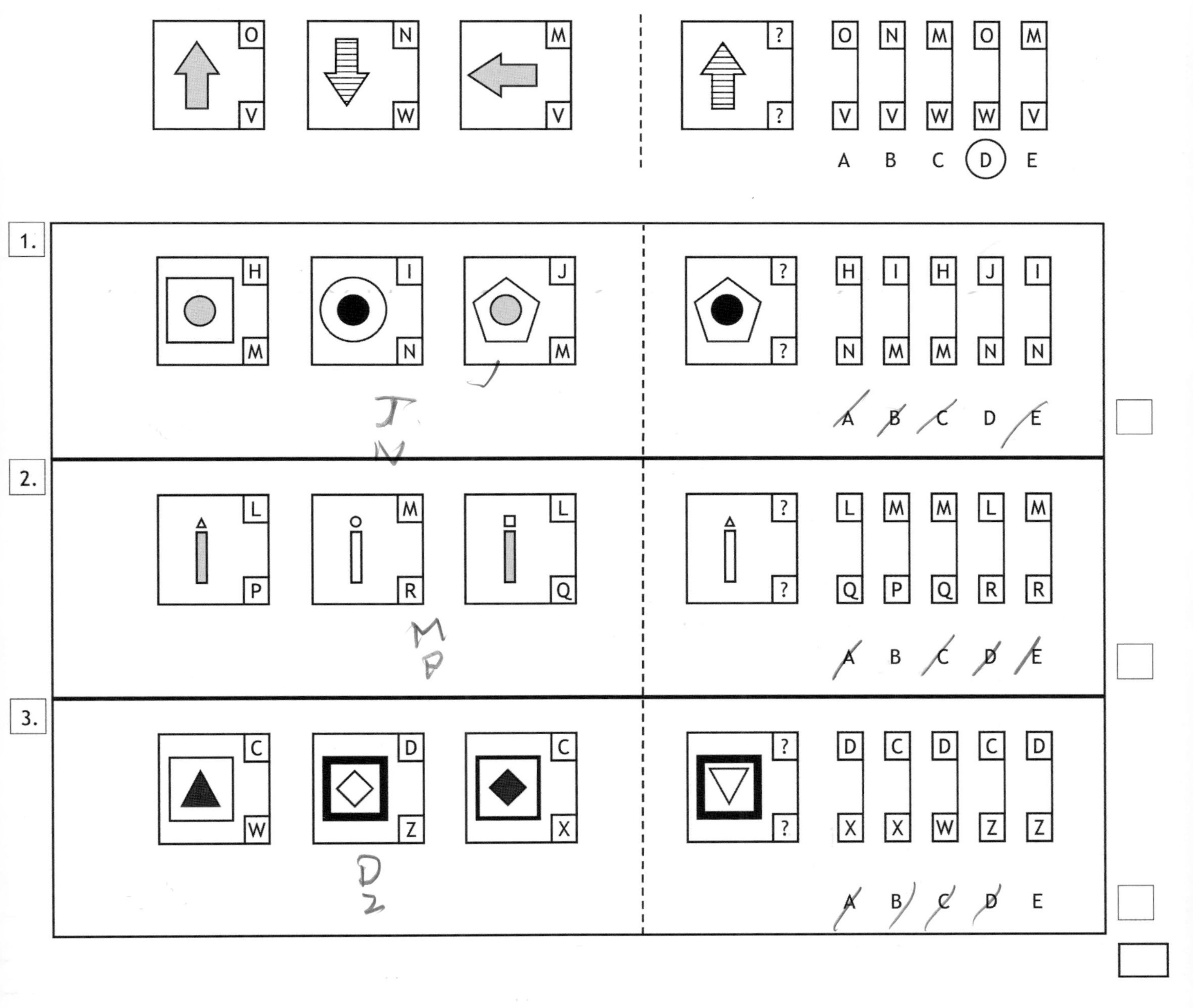

Page 7.2

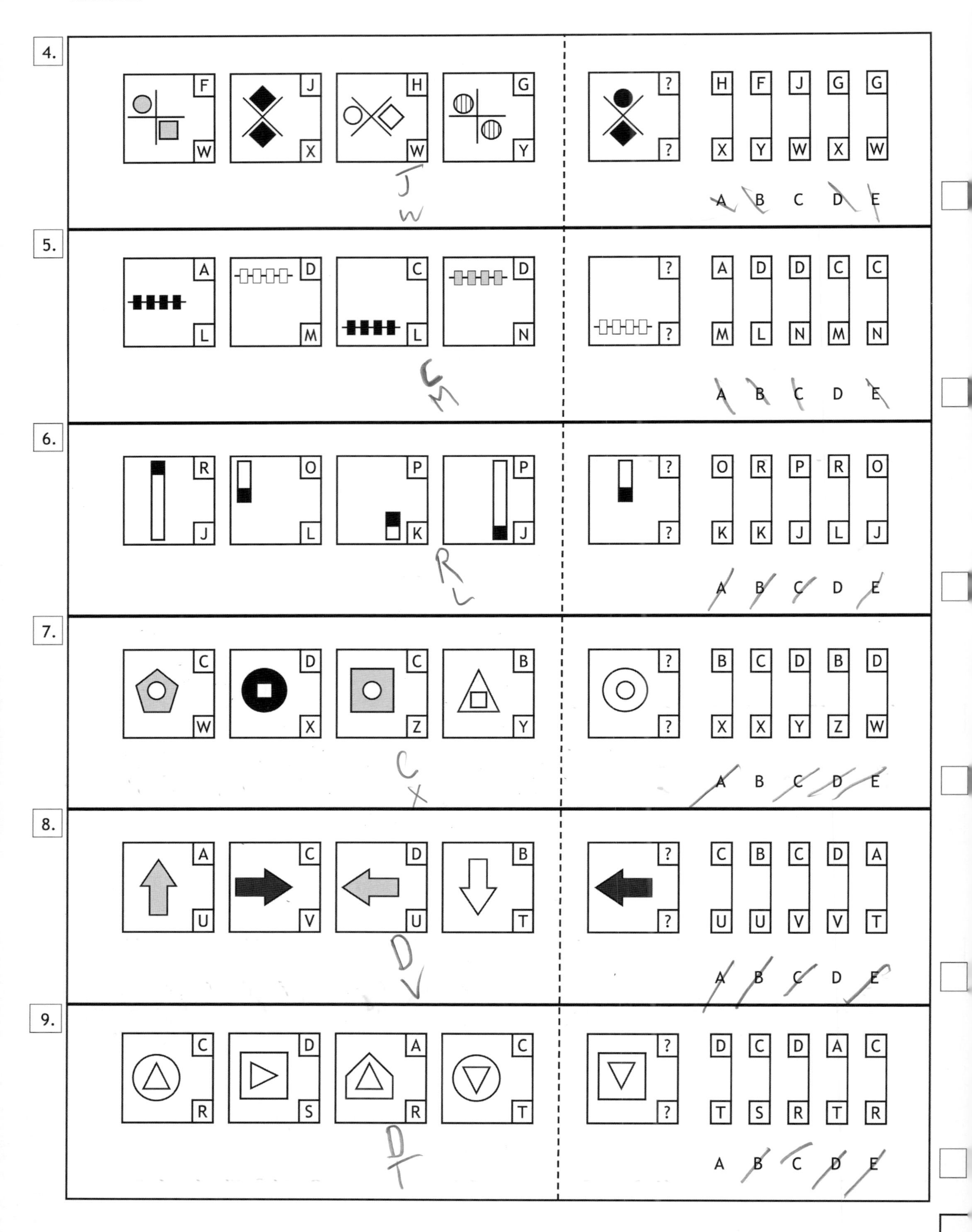

Section B

On the left of each question are two figures connected by an arrow. You must work out how the second figure is related to the first. Now look at the third figure. Which of the five other figures that follow is related to the third in the same way that the second is to the first?

Choose the shape that you think goes with the third shape and circle the letter on the answer sheet, or mark the appropriate box on the multiple choice answer sheet.

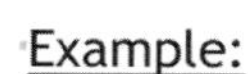

Example:

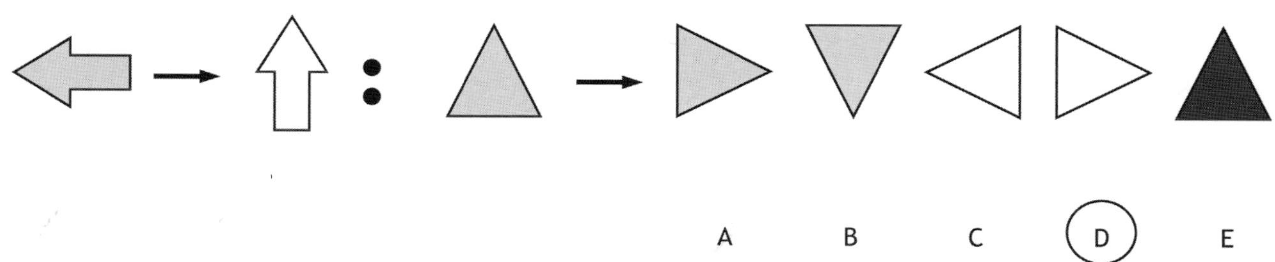

A B C D E

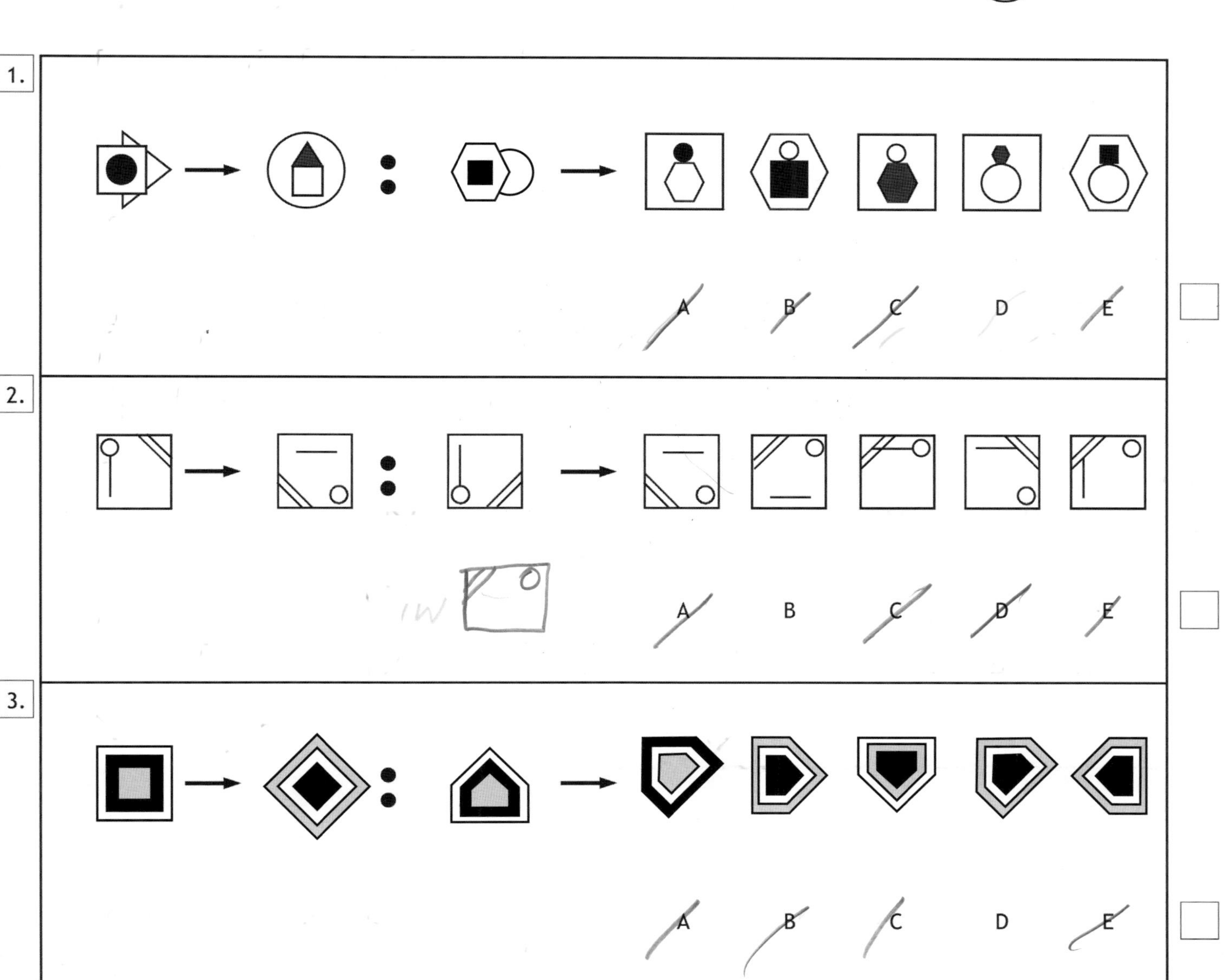

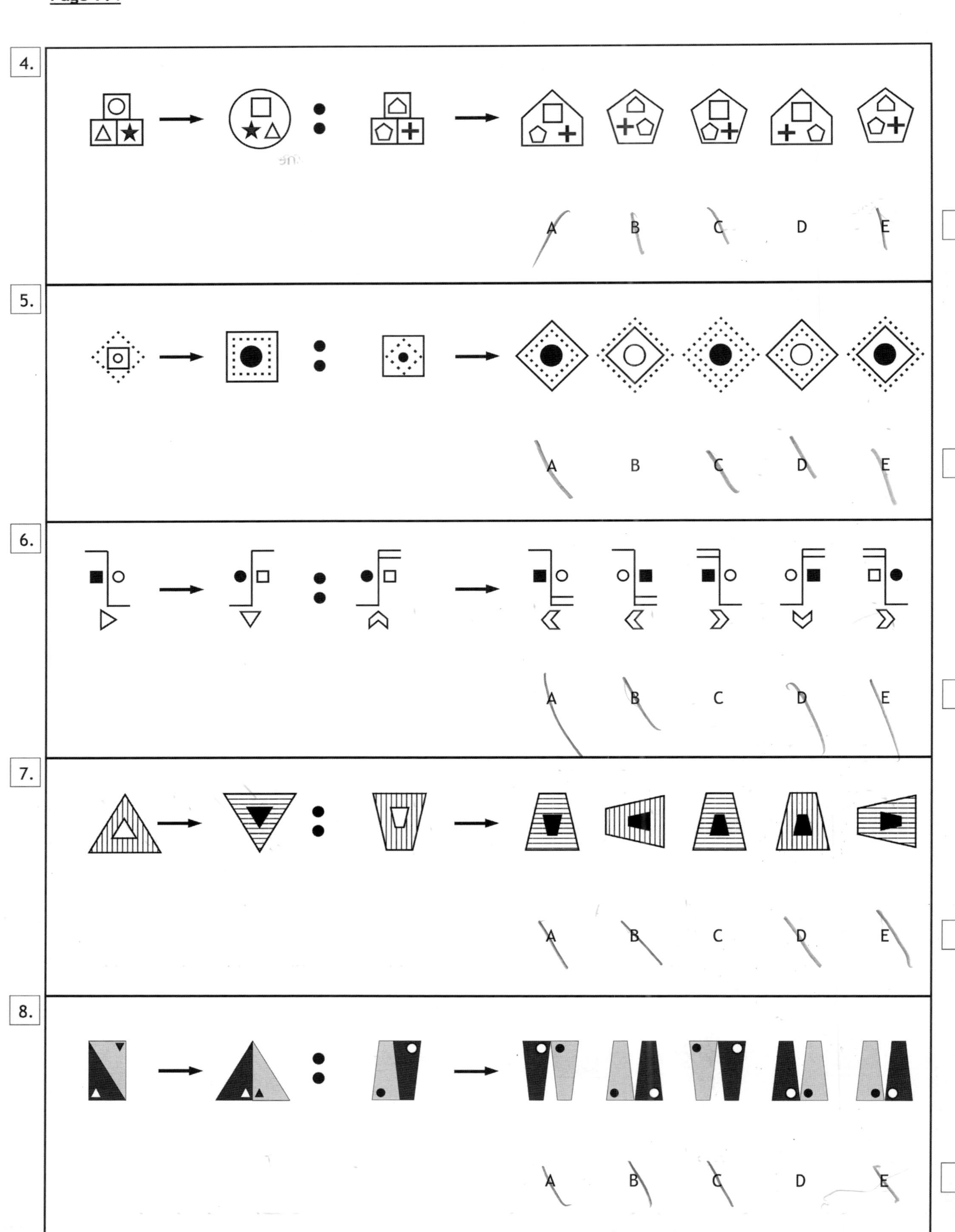
4.
A
B
C
D
E
5.
A
B
C
D
E
6.
A
B
C
D
E
7.
A
B
C
D
E
8.
A
B
C
D
E

Section C

There are figures drawn in three sections of the large square on the left hand side of the page. One of the small squares is empty. This square can be filled by only one of the five boxes on the right.

Choose the box that you think will best complete the large square and circle the letter on the answer sheet, or mark the appropriate box on the multiple choice answer sheet.

Example:

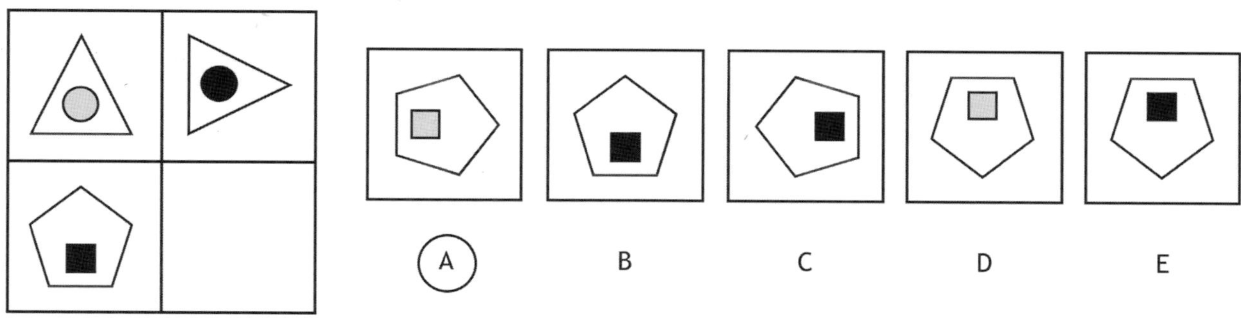

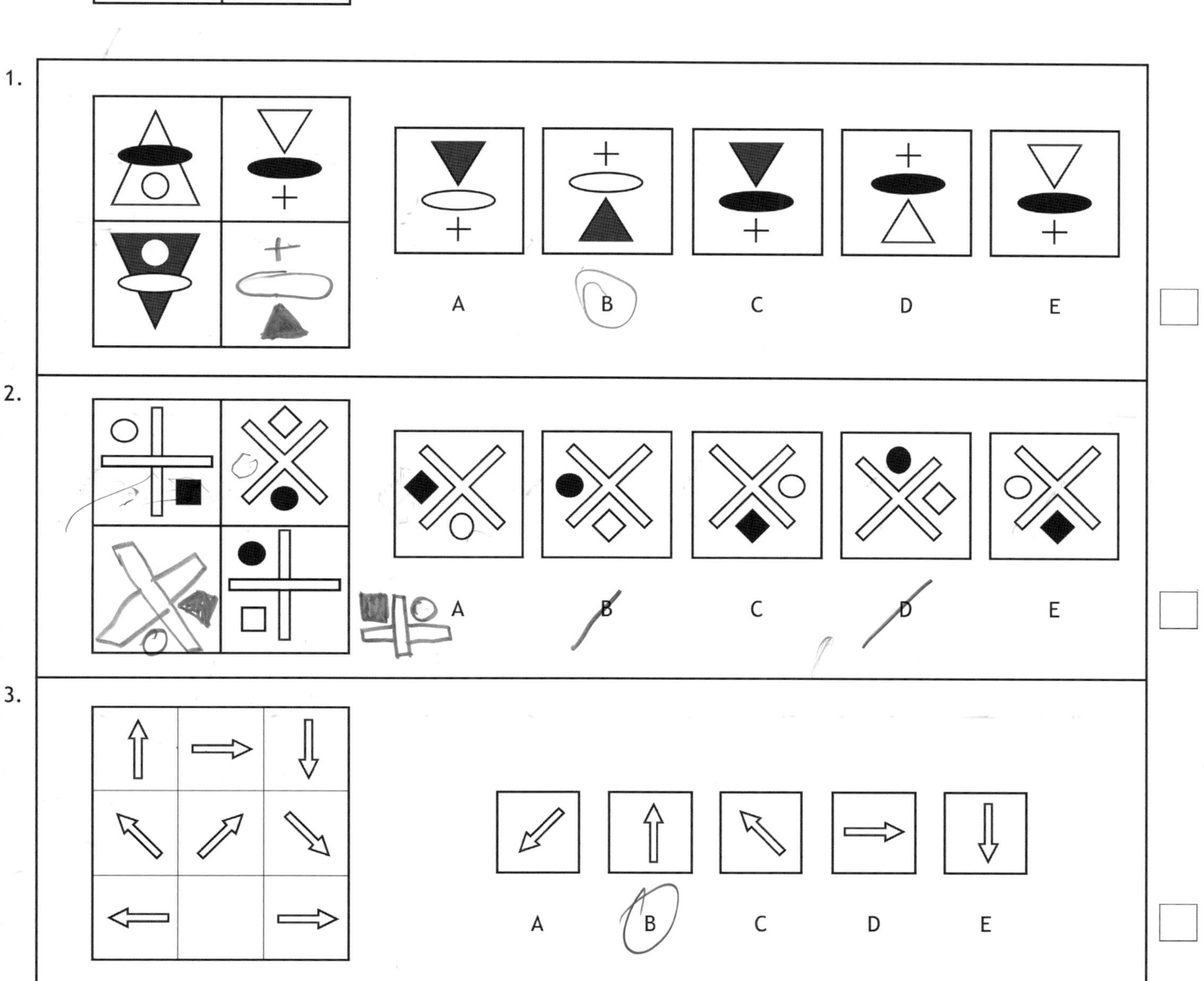

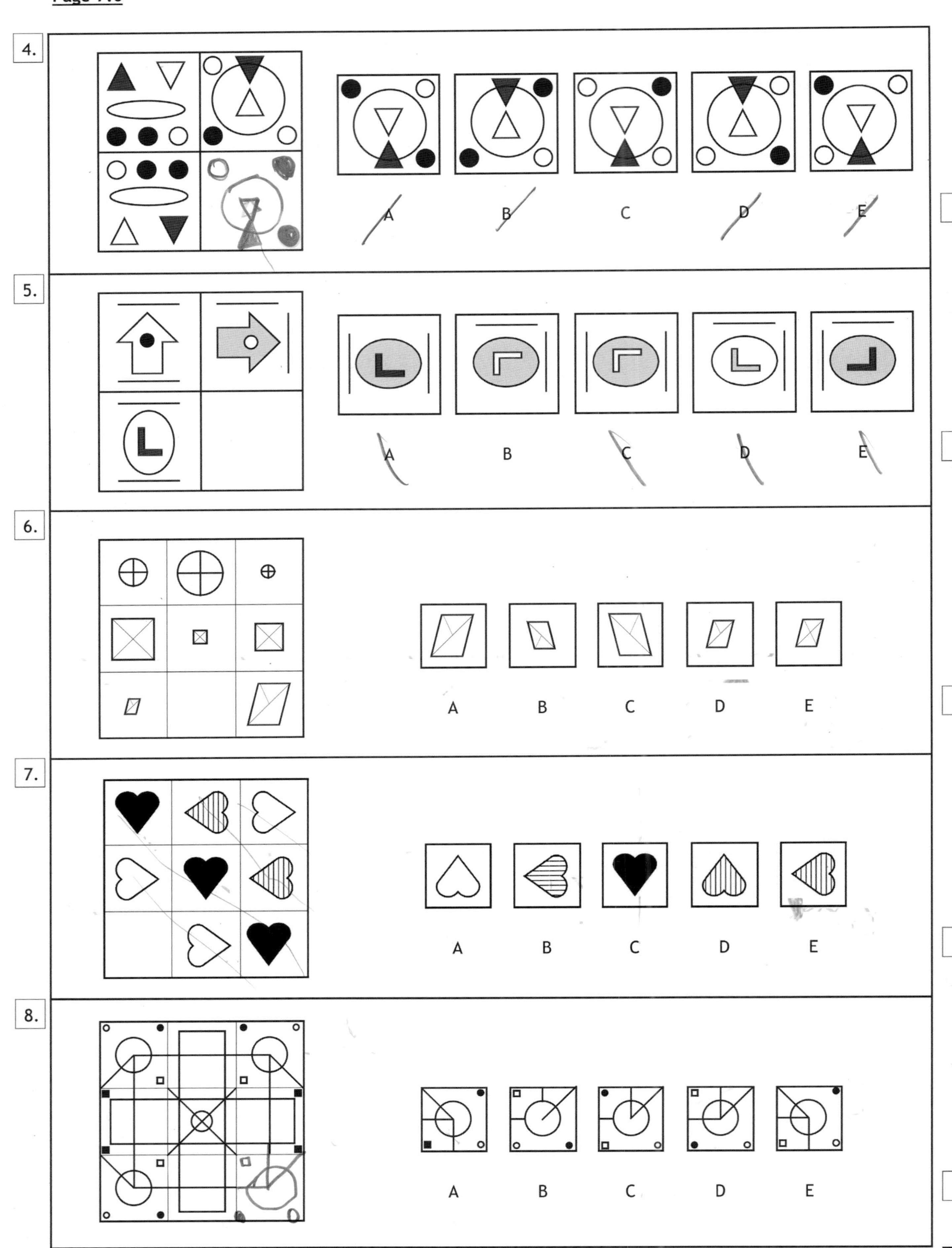
4.
A
B
C
D
E
5.
A
B
C
D
E
6.
A
B
C
D
E
7.
A
B
C
D
E
8.
A
B
C
D
E

Section D

On the left hand side of the page there are two shapes that are similar. On the right hand side there are five other shapes.

You must choose one shape of the five that you is most alike to the first two and circle its letter on the answer sheet, or mark the appropriate box on the multiple choice answer sheet.

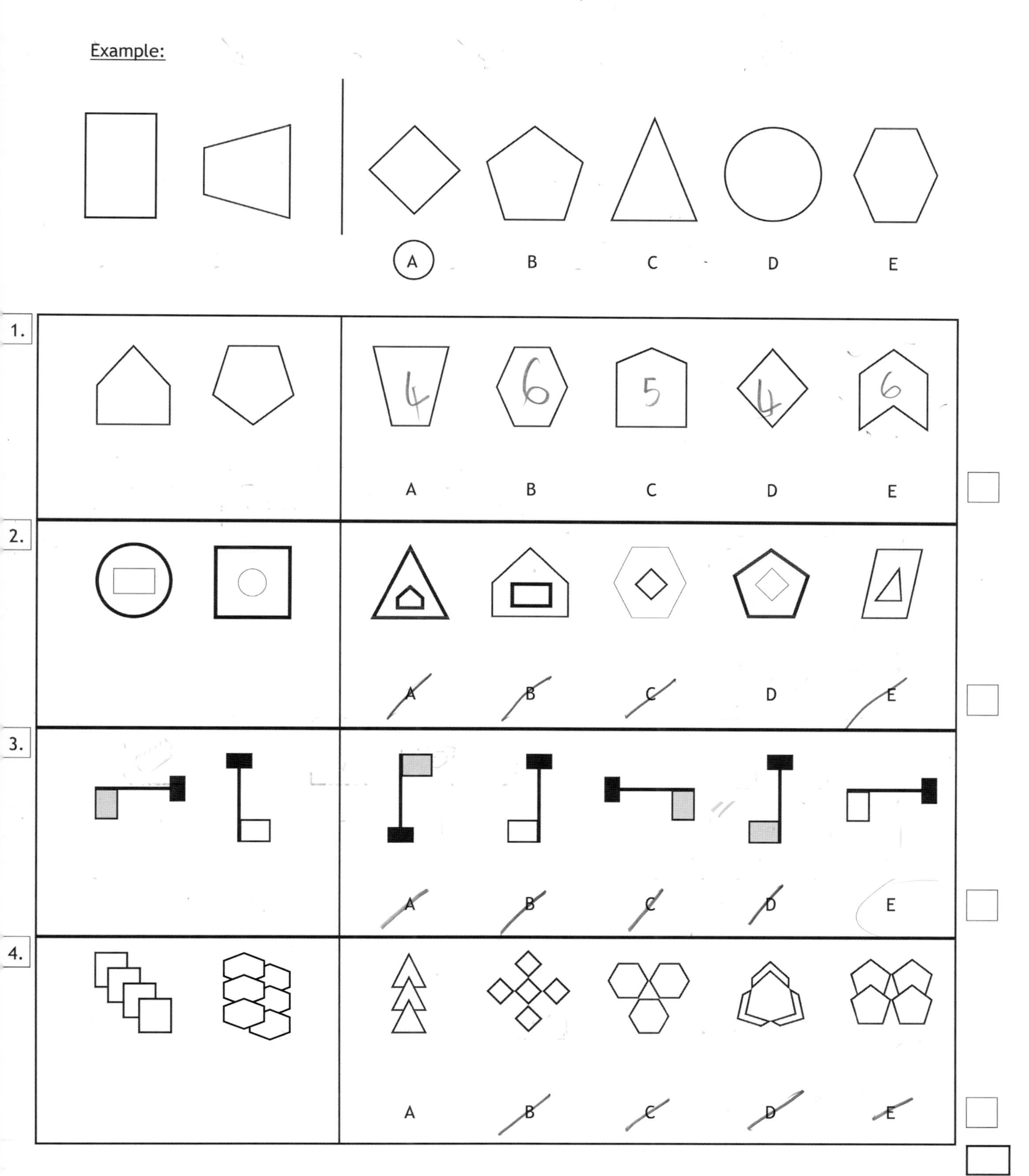

Page 7.8

5.

A B C D E

6.

A B C D E

7.

A B C D E

8.

A B C D E

9.

A B C D E

10.

A B C D E

Practice Paper 8.

There are 35 questions in four sections on this paper. You have 30 minutes to complete this test.

Circle your answers carefully on the answer sheet or place a mark in the multiple choice answer box on the separate sheet.

Section A

On the left hand side of the page there are two shapes that are similar. On the right hand side there are five other shapes.

You must choose one shape of the five that you is most alike to the first two and circle its letter on the answer sheet, or mark the appropriate box on the multiple choice answer sheet.

Example:

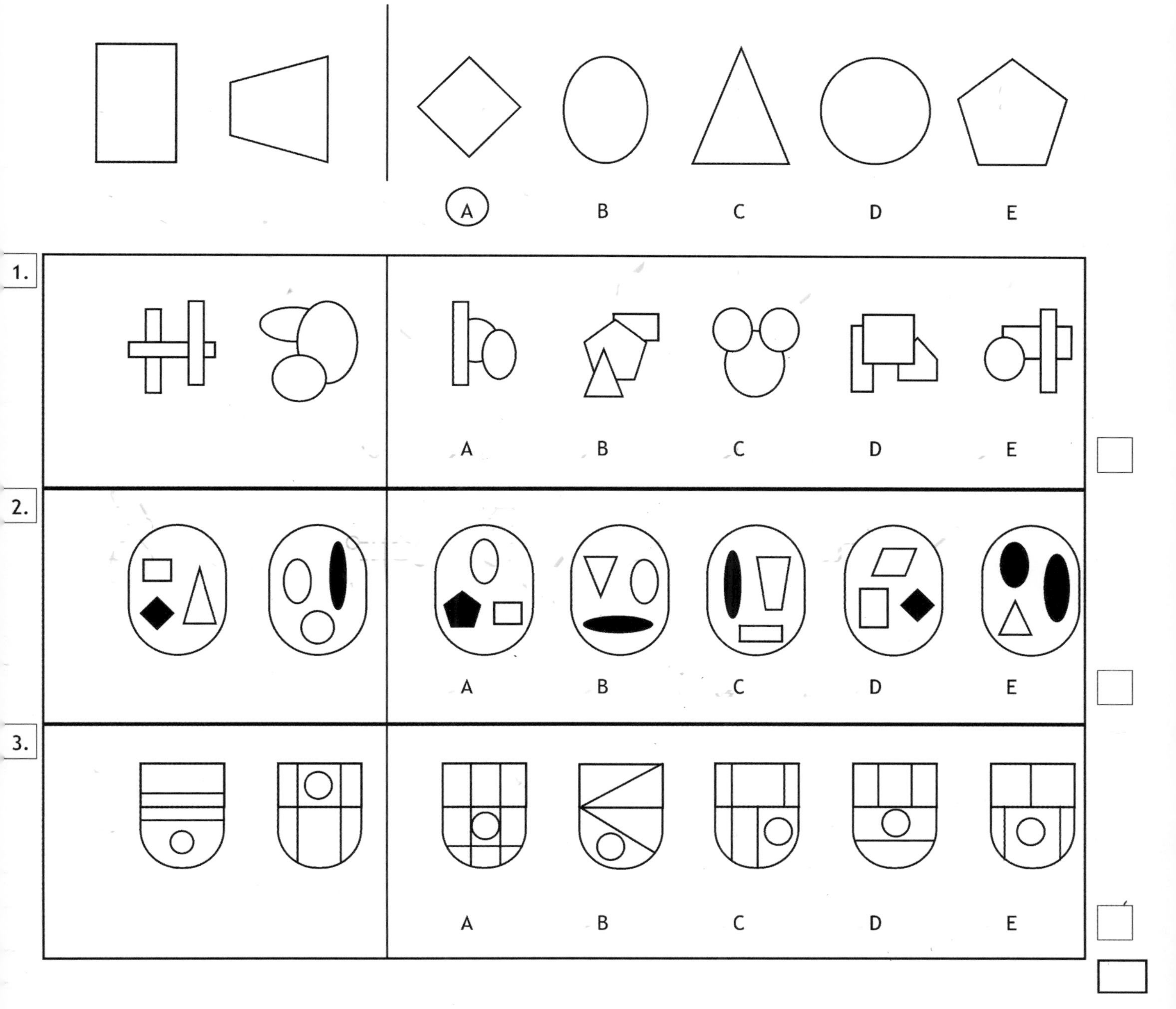

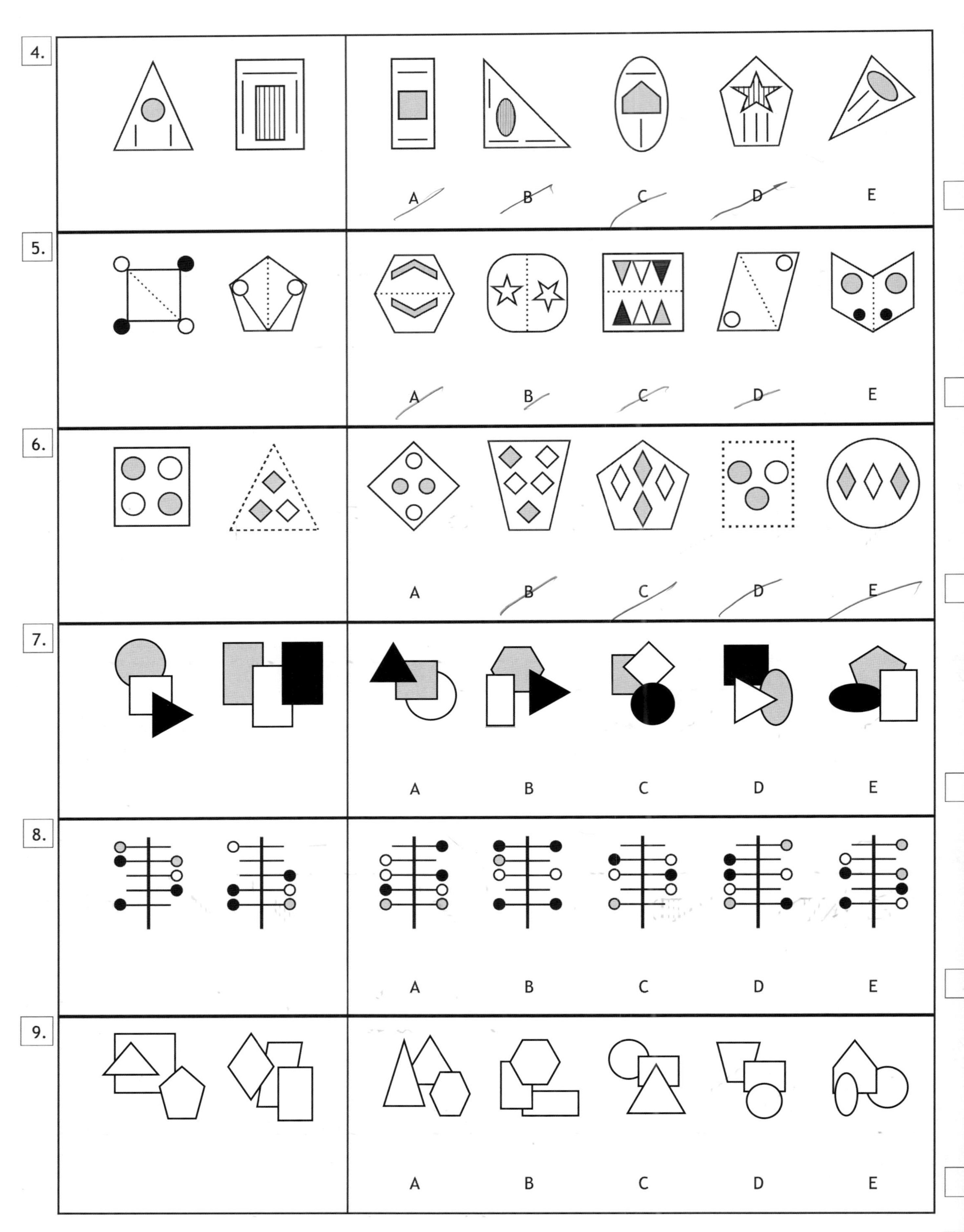

4.
A
B
C
D
E
5.
A
B
C
D
E
6.
A
B
C
D
E
7.
A
B
C
D
E
8.
A
B
C
D
E
9.
A
B
C
D
E

Section B

On the left of the page is a sequence of figures in five boxes. One of the boxes is empty. This box can be filled by only one of the figures in the five boxes on the right.

Choose the figure that you think will best complete the sequence and circle the letter on the answer sheet, or mark the appropriate box on the multiple choice answer sheet.

Example:

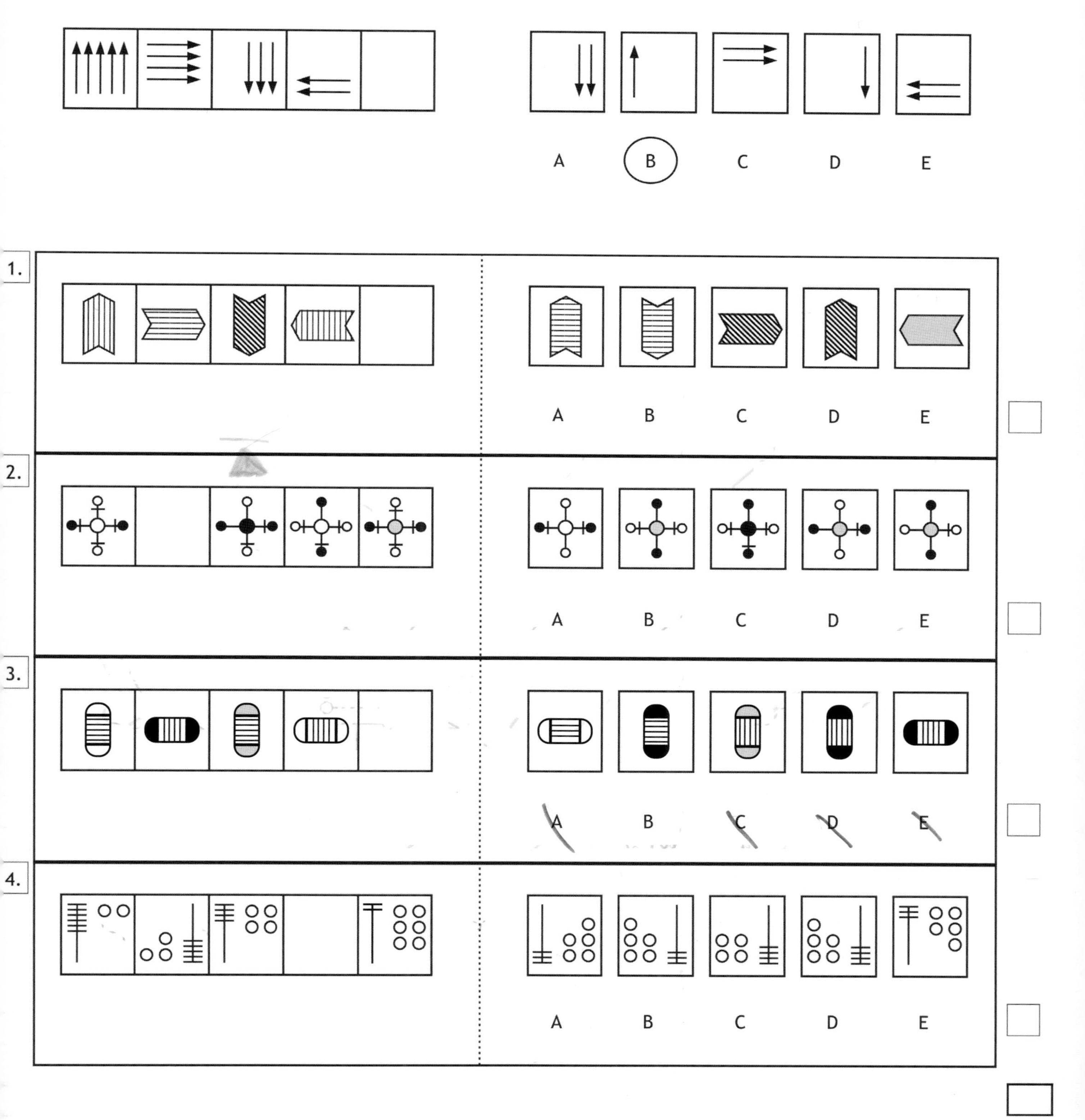

Page 8.4

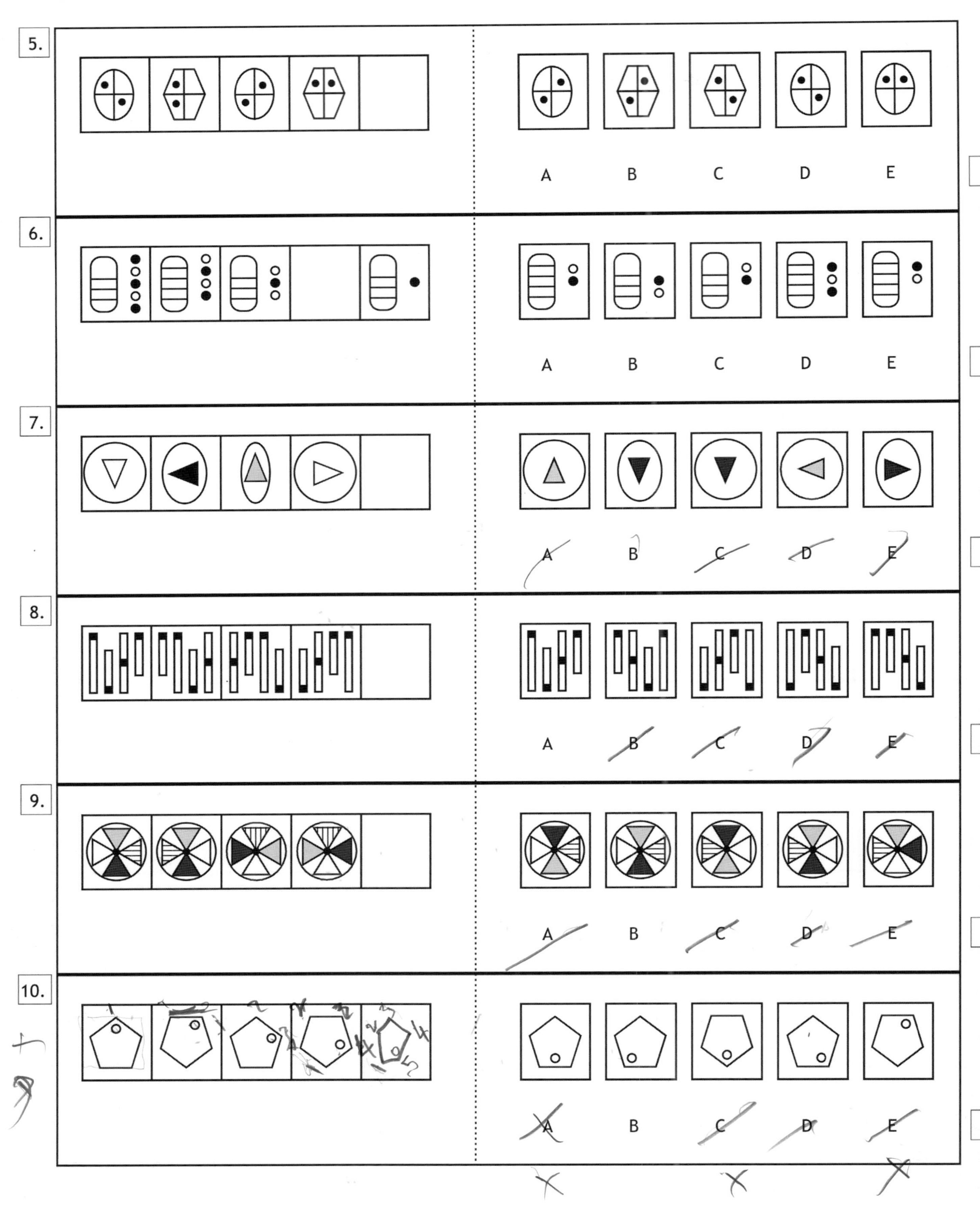

Section C

Each of the following questions consists of five shapes in a row. They all have something in common, except one. You must find the odd one out.

Choose the shape that you think does not go with the other four and circle the letter on the answer sheet, or mark the appropriate box on the multiple choice answer sheet.

Example:

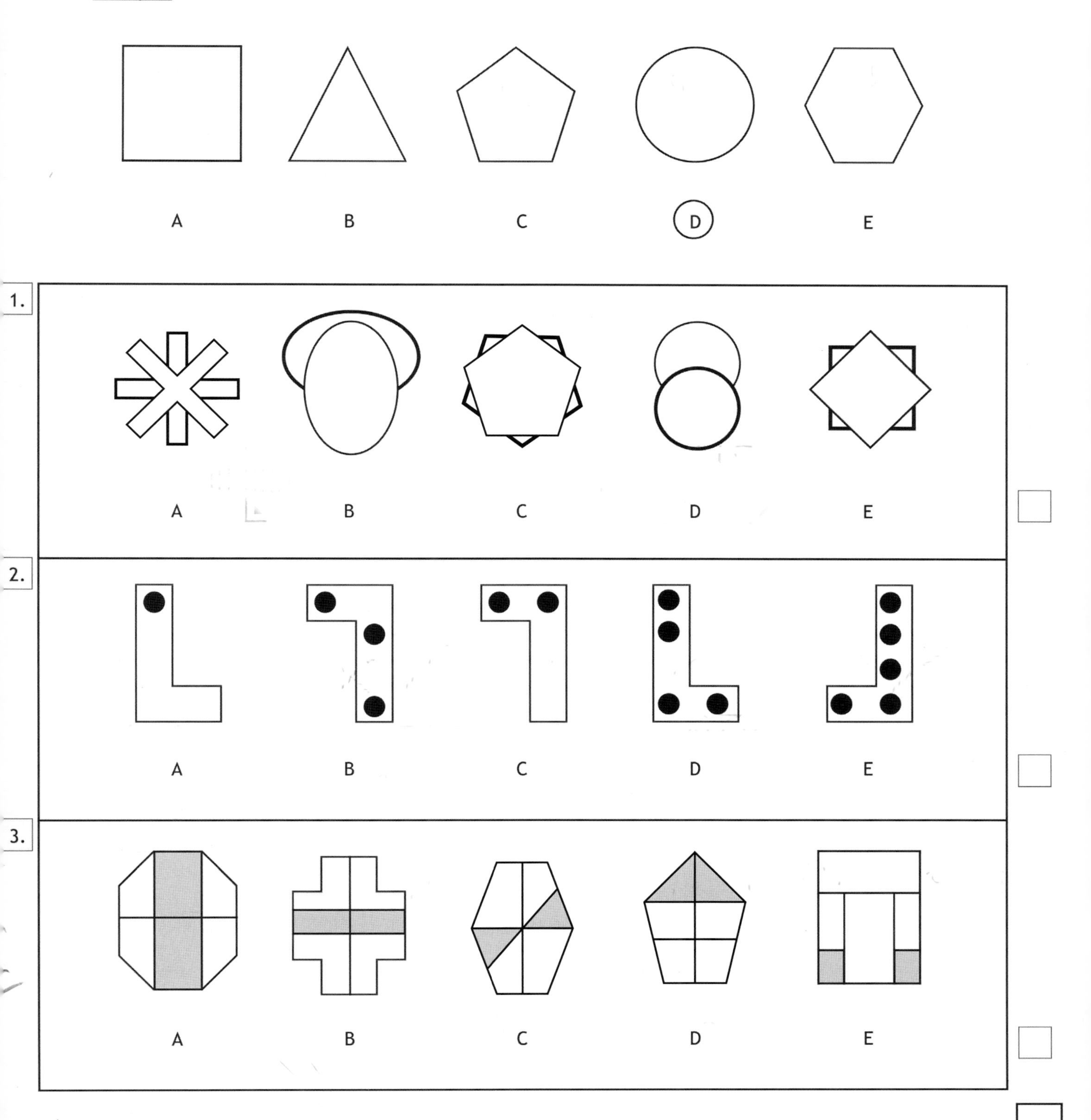

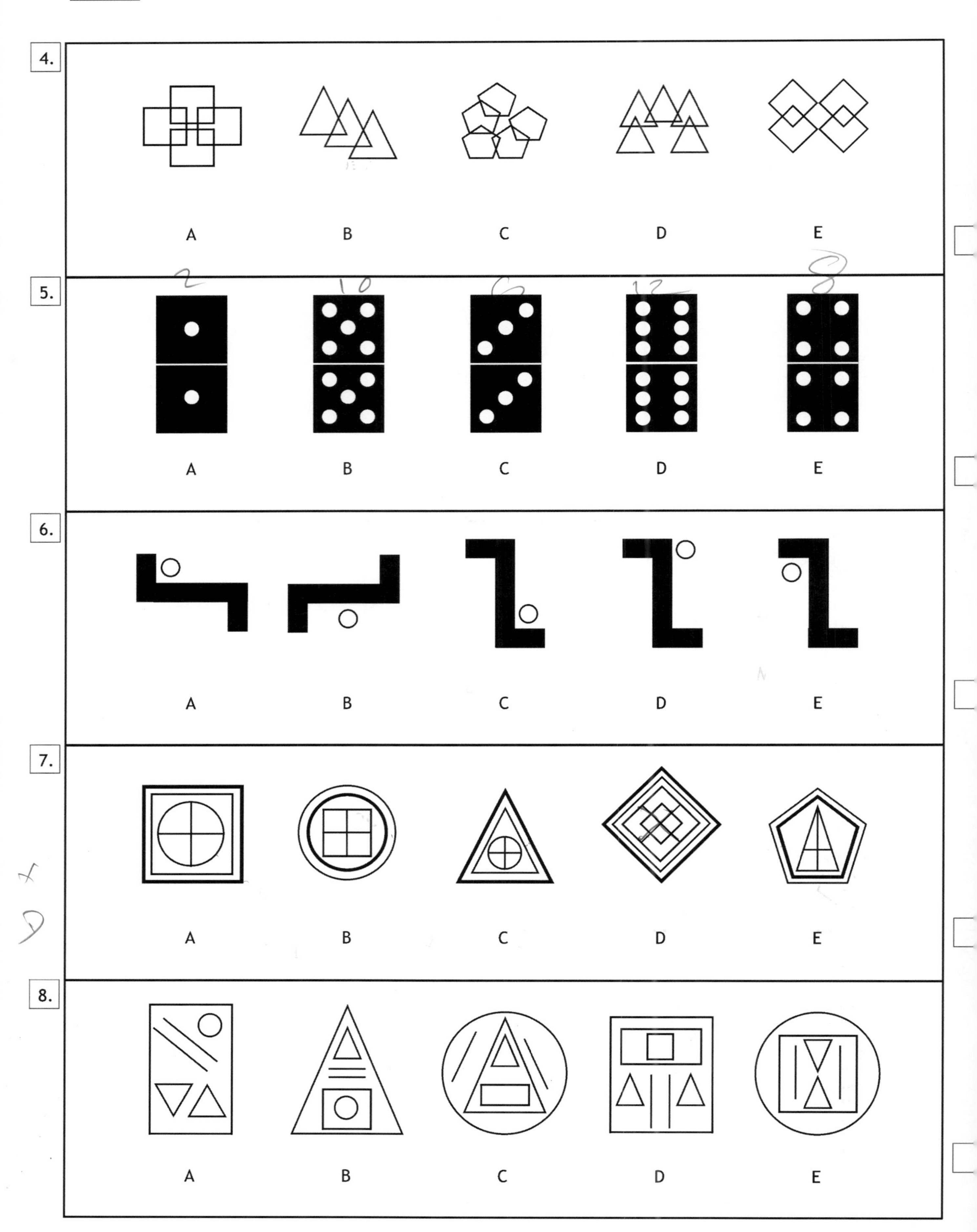
4.
A
B
C
D
E
5.
A
B
C
D
E
6.
A
B
C
D
E
7.
A
B
C
D
E
8.
A
B
C
D
E

Section D

The shapes drawn on the left hand side of the page have been given letter codes that describe certain aspects of their appearance. Using this information you can find the code for the single shape.

Choose the code that you think describes the single shape and circle the letter on the answer sheet, or mark the appropriate box on the multiple choice answer sheet.

Example:

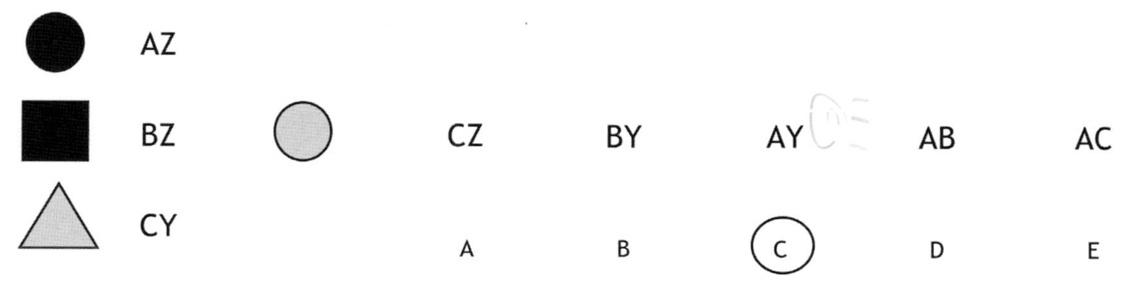

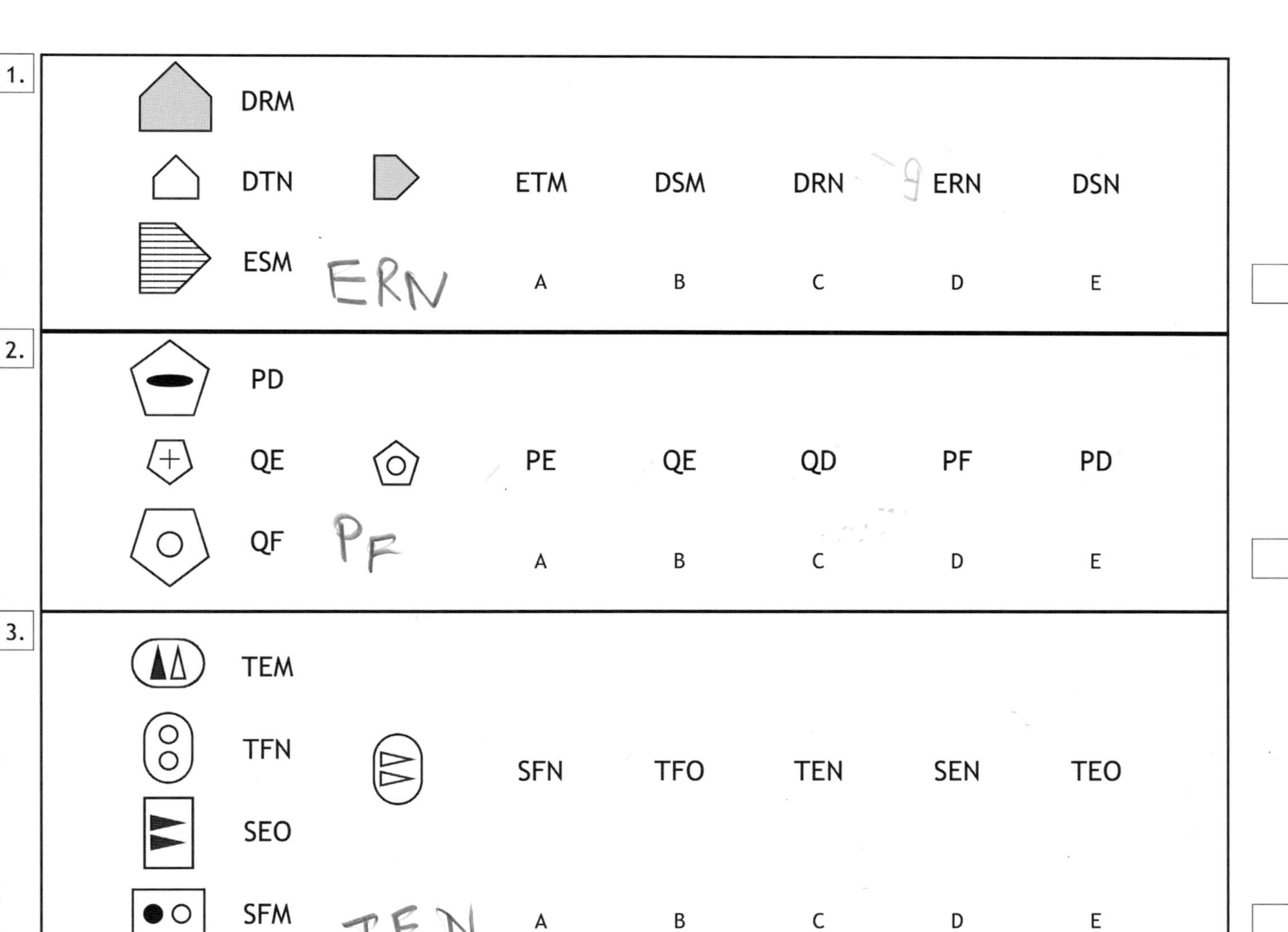

Page 8.8

4.

			A	B	C	D	E
	GL						
	FM		EL	FL	EM	GM	GL
	EL	EM					

5.

			A	B	C	D	E
	EP						
	FO		EQ	FP	FO	EO	EP
	FQ	EO					

6.

			A	B	C	D	E
	AJW						
	DHX		DJW	BJX	AHW	DFY	BGY
	AGY						
	BFW	BJX					

7.

			A	B	C	D	E
	BRH						
	ATF		ASF	BQG	BTG	ARG	BSF
	BSG	BTG					
	AQG						

8.

			A	B	C	D	E
	TWB						
	RXC		TXD	SXB	TWC	SXD	RWC
	SWD						
	TXC	SXB					

Paper 5

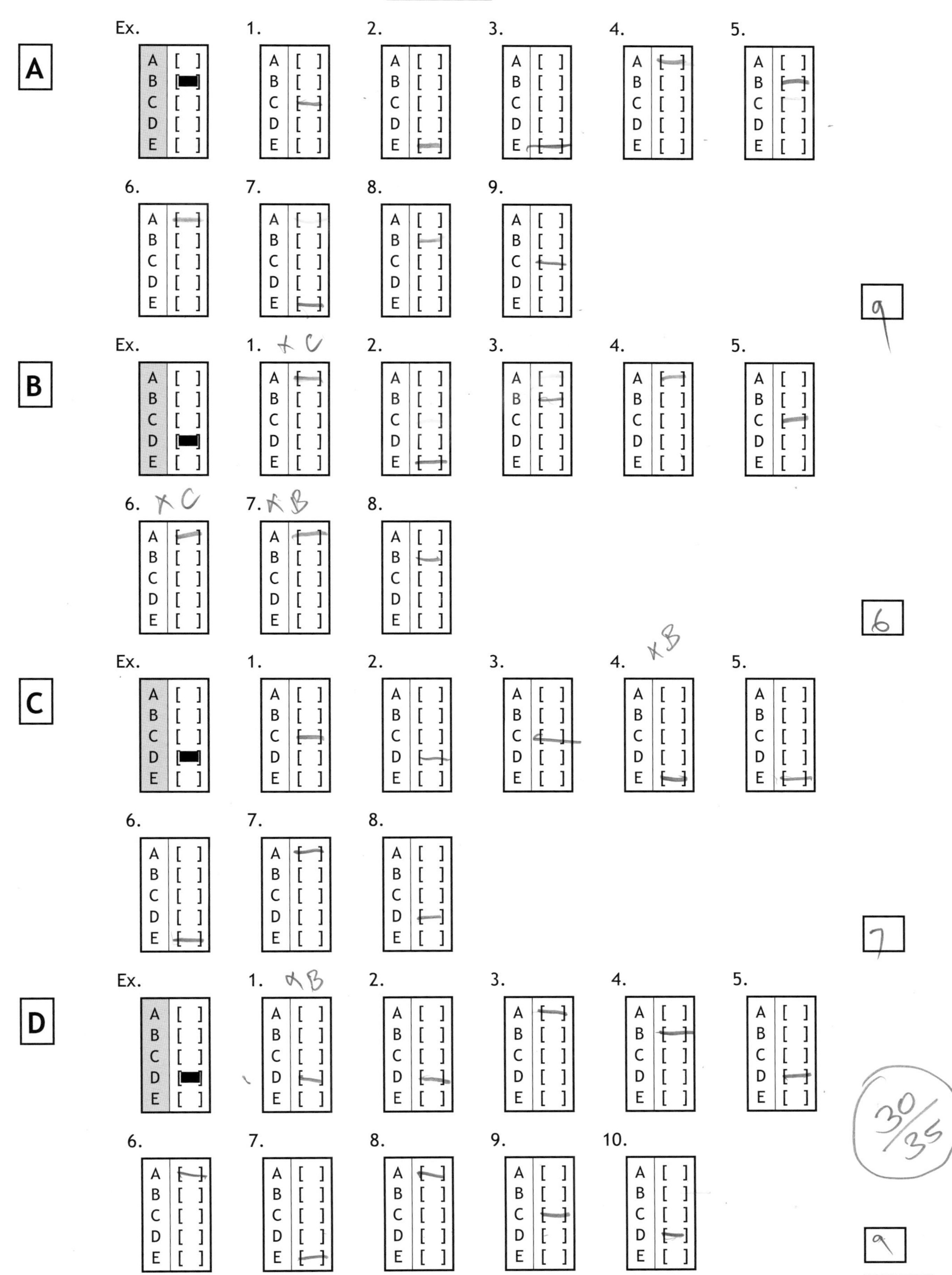

Paper 6

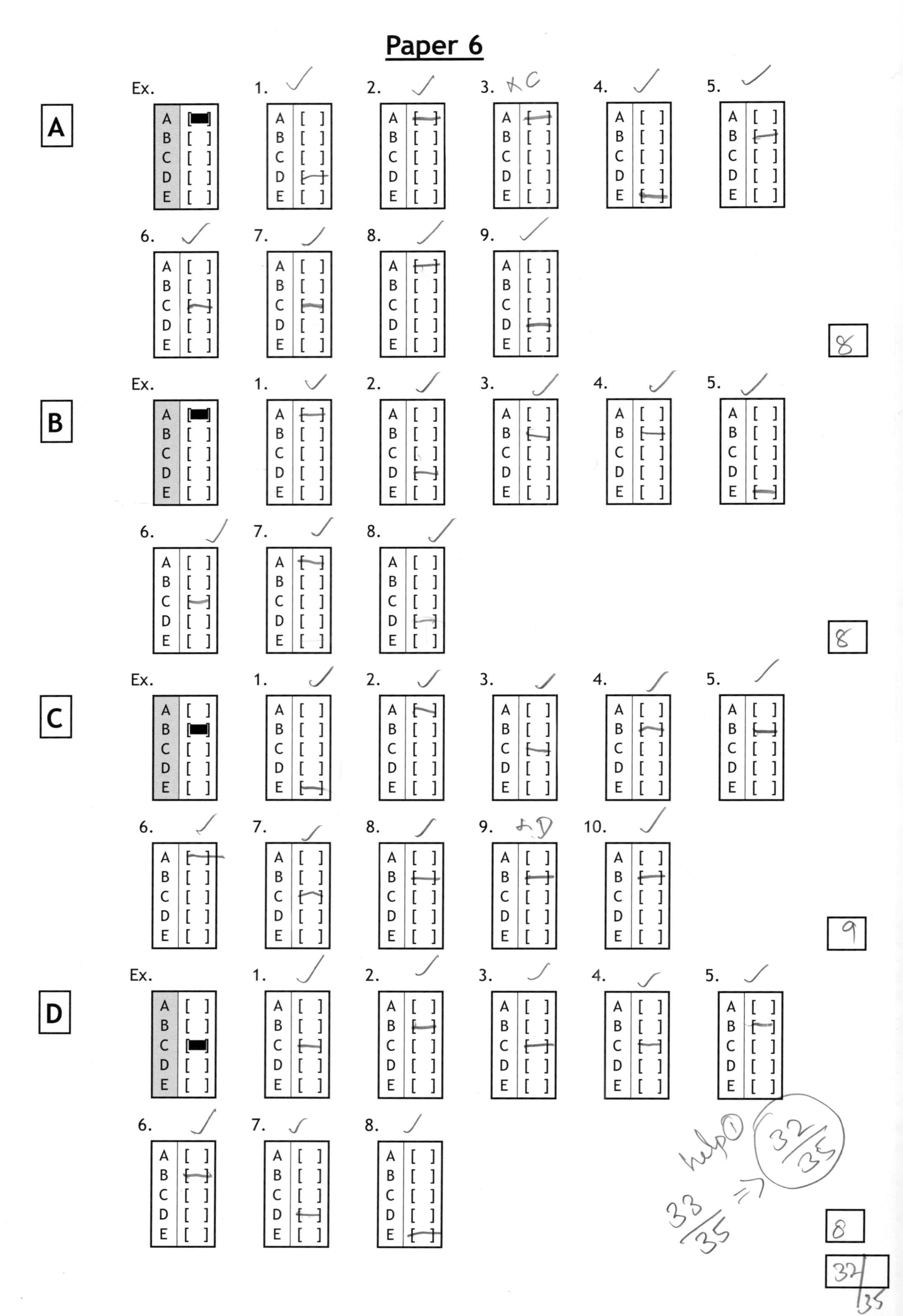

Non-Verbal Reasoning - Multiple Choice Answer Sheets

Paper 1

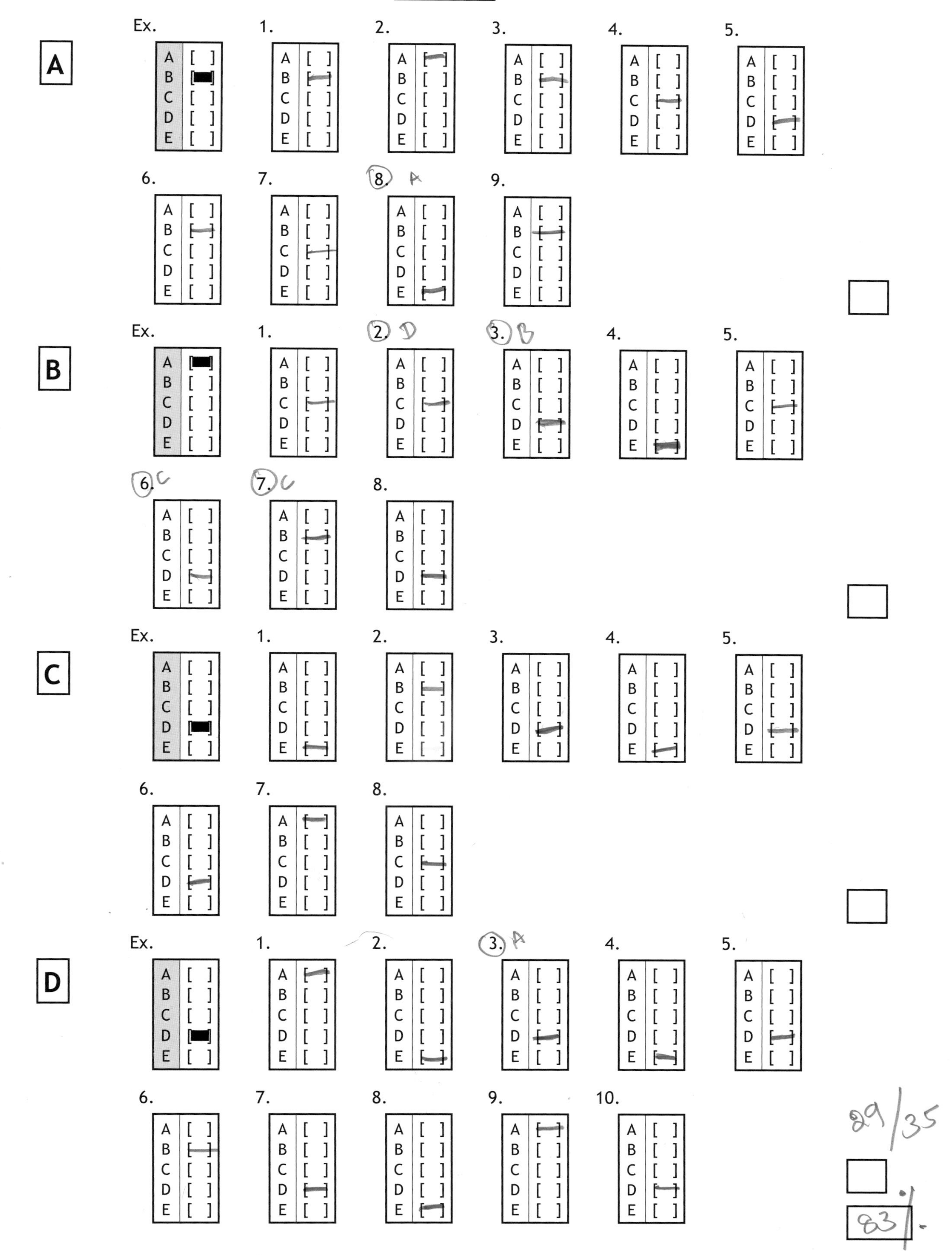

Paper 2

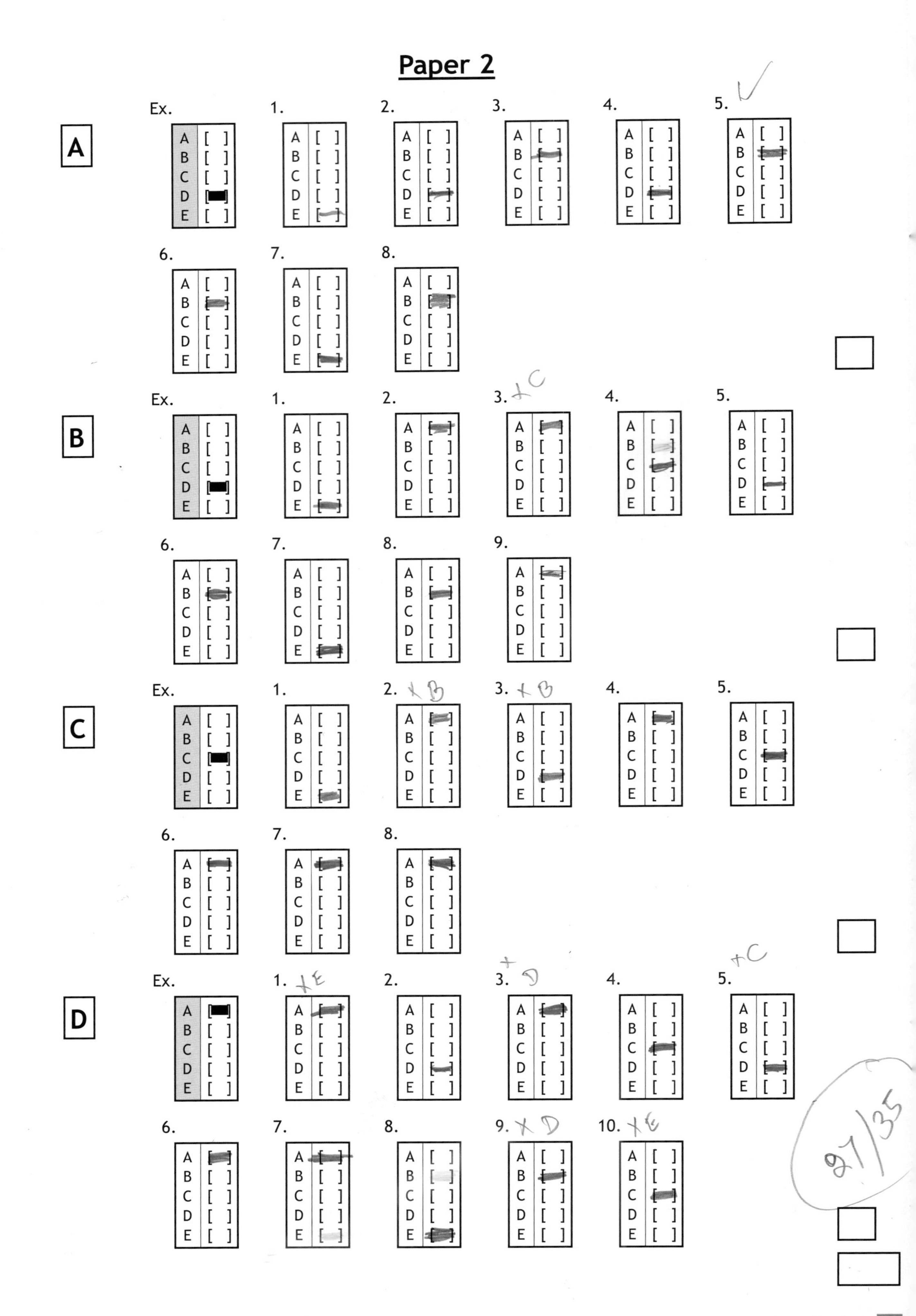

Paper 3

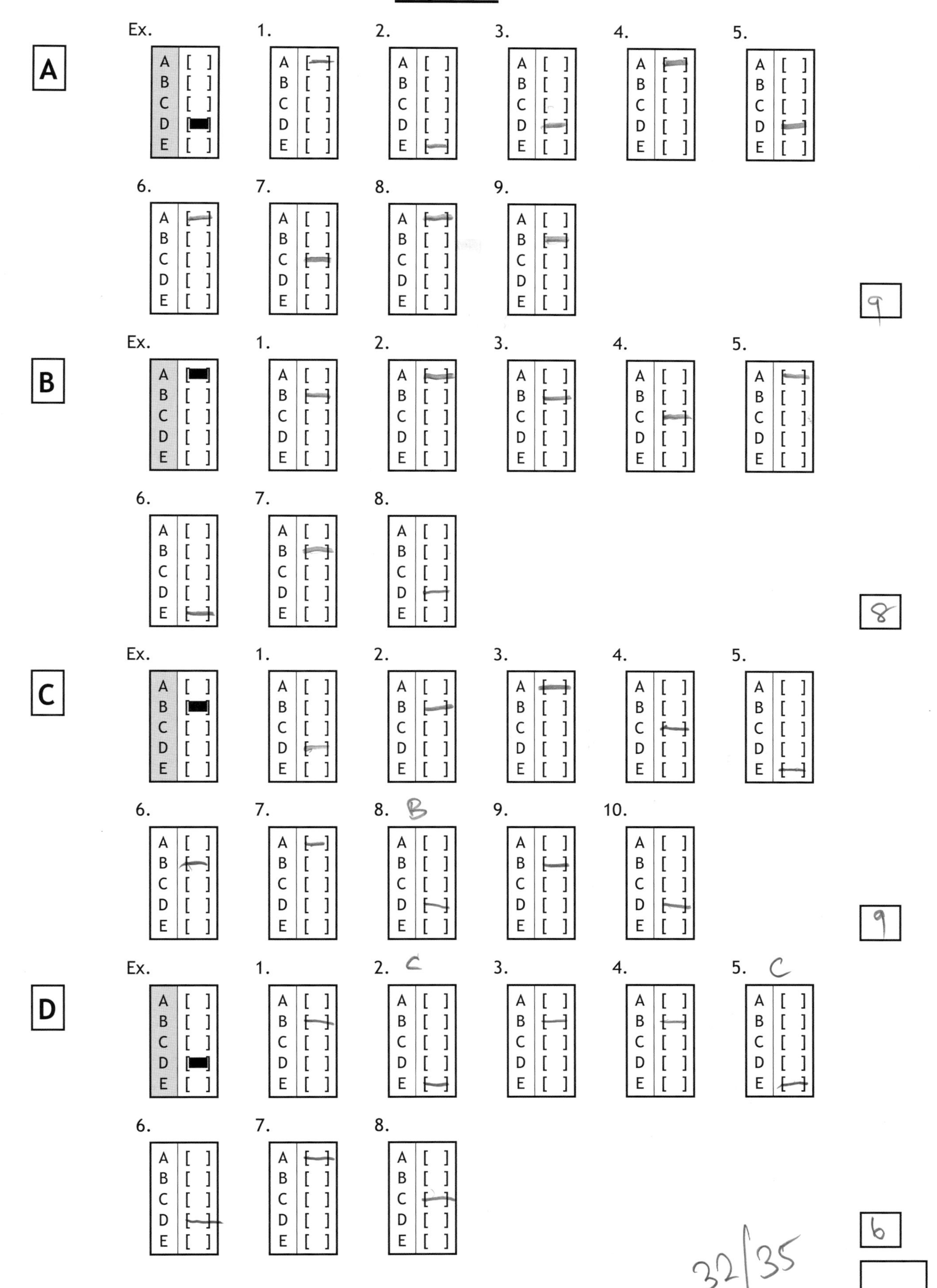

Paper 4

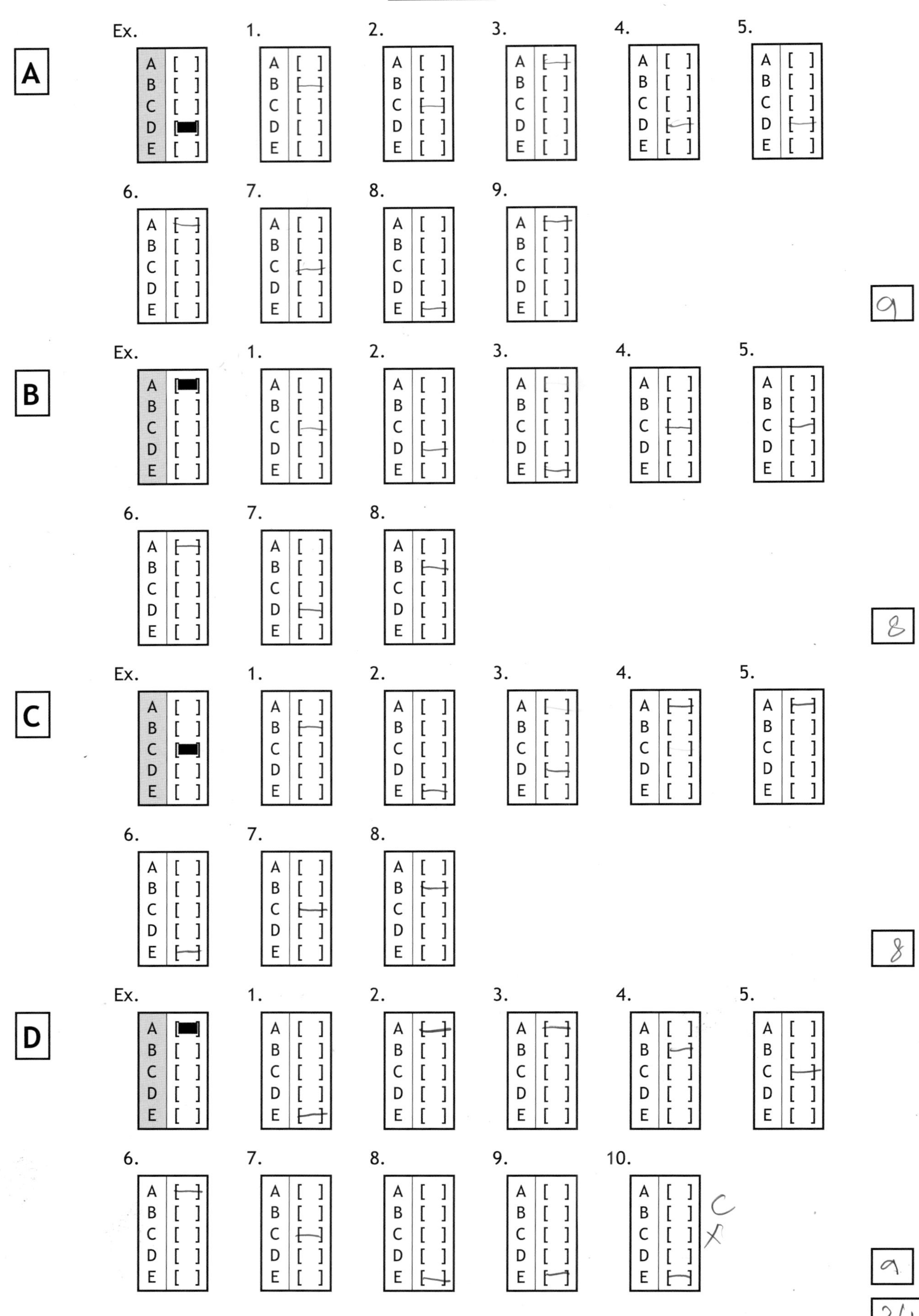

Progress table

	Total number of correct	Questions attempted	Time taken to complete	
Paper 1	29	35		83%
Paper 2	27	35		77%
Paper 3	32	35		91%
Paper 4	34	35		97%
Paper 5	30	35		86%
Paper 6	32	35		91%
Paper 7	32	35		91%
Paper 8	32	35		91%

Non-Verbal Reasoning - Answers

Paper 1

	A	B	C	D
1	B	C	E	A
2	A	D	B	E
3	B	B	D	A
4	C	E	E	E
5	D	C	D	D
6	B	C	D	B
7	C	C	A	D
8	A	D	C	E
9	B			A
10				D

Paper 2

	A	B	C	D
1	E	E	E	E
2	D	A	B	D
3	B	C	B	D
4	D	C	A	C
5	B	D	C	C
6	B	B	A	A
7	E	E	A	A
8	B	B	A	E
9		A		D
10				E

Paper 3

	A	B	C	D
1	A	B	D	B
2	E	A	B	C
3	D	B	A	B
4	A	C	C	B
5	D	A	E	C
6	A	E	B	D
7	C	B	A	A
8	A	D	B	C
9	B		B	
10			D	

Paper 4

	A	B	C	D
1	B	C	B	E
2	C	D	E	A
3	A	E	D	A
4	D	C	A	B
5	D	C	A	C
6	A	A	E	A
7	C	D	C	C
8	E	B	B	E
9	A			E
10				C

Paper 5

	A	B	C	D
1	C	C	C	B
2	E	E	D	D
3	E	B	C	A
4	A	A	B	B
5	B	C	E	D
6	A	C	E	A
7	E	B	A	E
8	B	B	D	A
9	C			C
10				D

Paper 6

	A	B	C	D
1	D	A	E	C
2	A	D	A	B
3	C	B	C	C
4	E	B	B	C
5	B	E	B	B
6	C	C	A	B
7	C	A	C	D
8	A	D	B	E
9	D		D	
10			B	

Paper 7

	A	B	C	D
1	D	A	B	C
2	B	B	A	D
3	E	D	B	E
4	C	D	C	A
5	D	B	B	C
6	D	C	D	C
7	A	C	E	D
8	D	E	D	B
9	A			E
10				A

Paper 8

	A	B	C	D
1	B	A	D	D
2	D	E	E	D
3	B	B	C	C
4	E	B	D	C
5	E	D	C	D
6	A	E	A	B
7	C	B	D	C
8	C	A	D	B
9	A	B		
10		D		

Paper 8

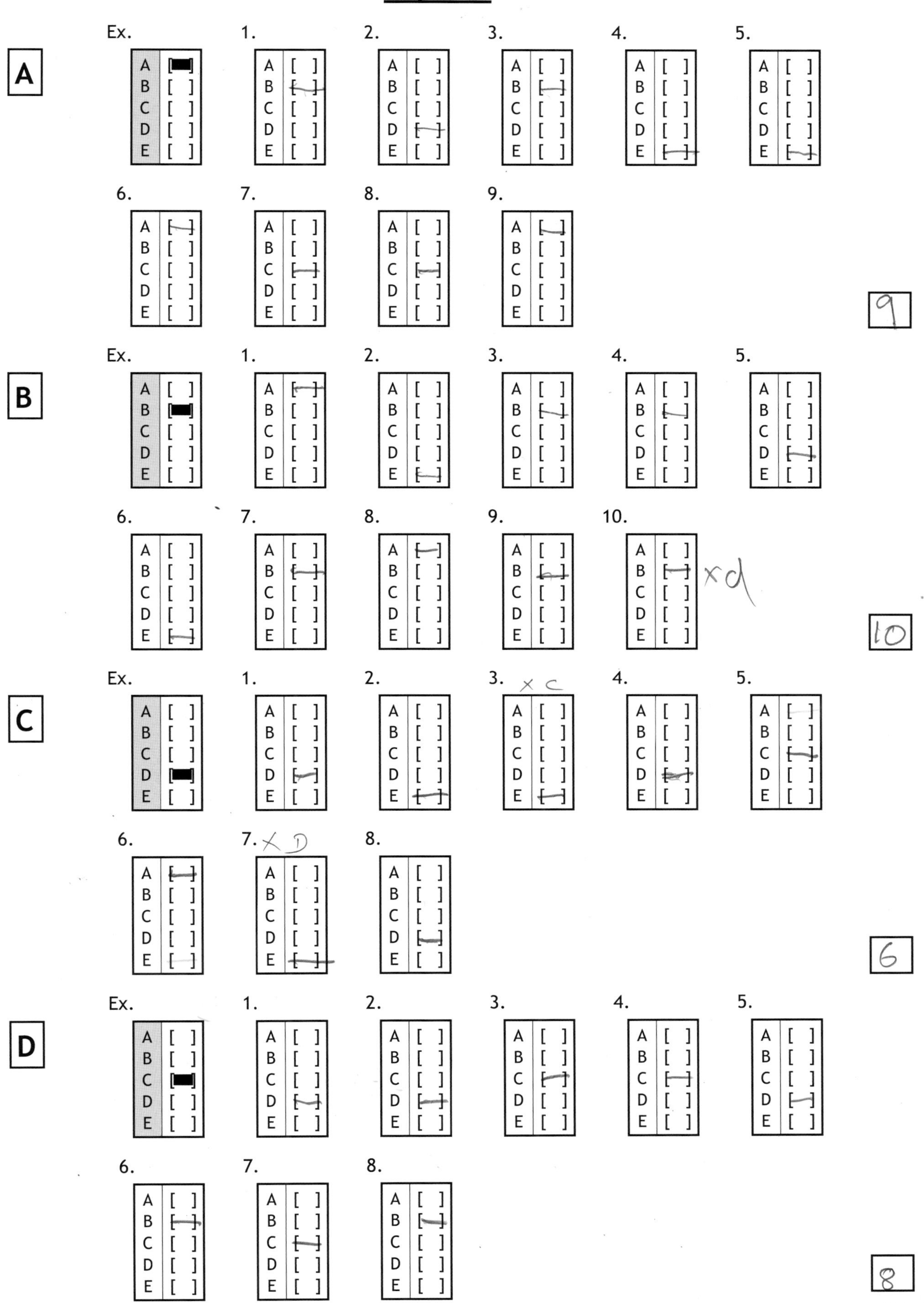

Paper 7

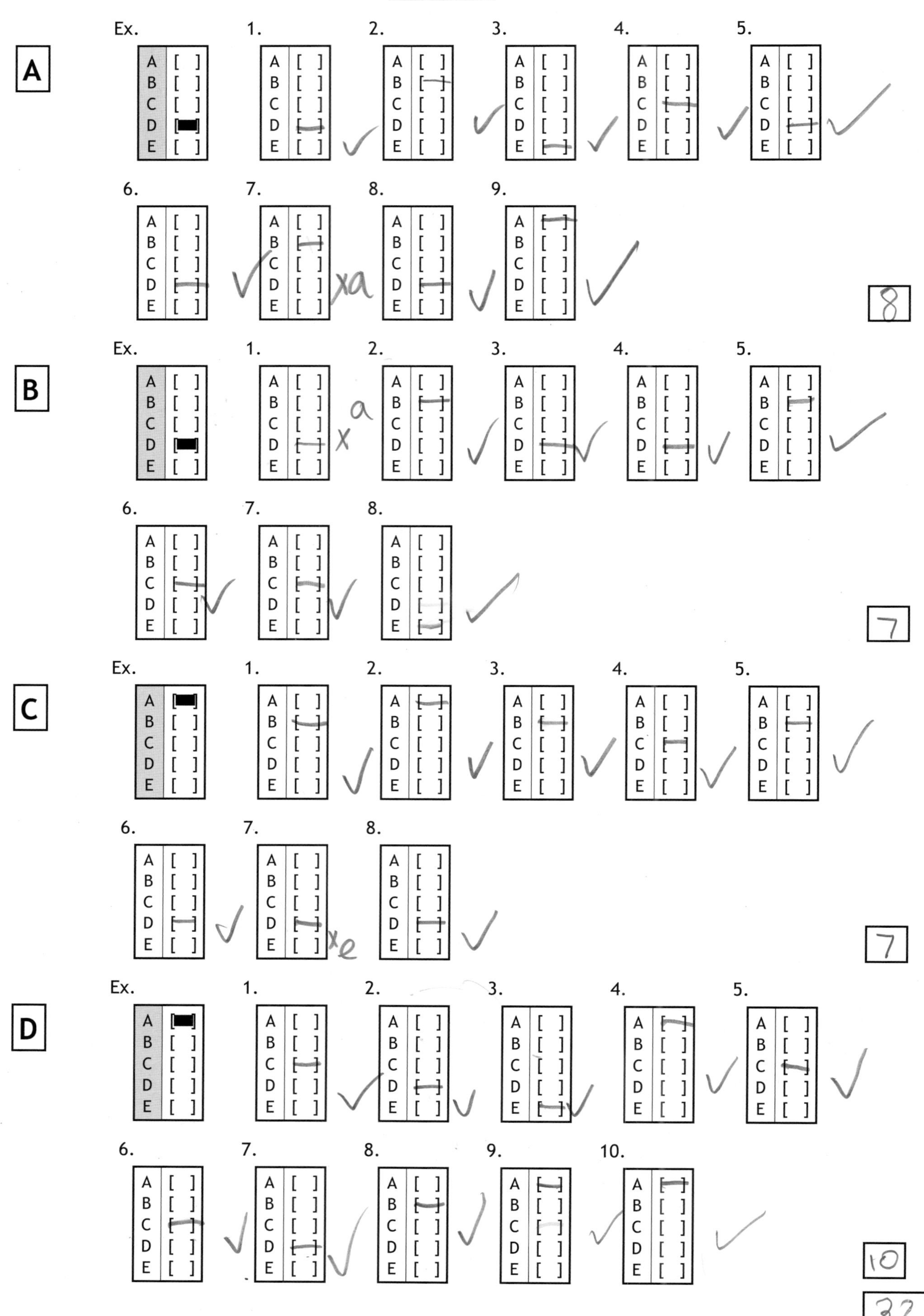